WriteTraits®

STUDENT TRAITBOOK

Vicki Spandel • Jeff Hicks

Vicki Spandel

Vicki Spandel was codirector of the original teacher team that developed the six-trait model and has designed instructional materials for all grade levels. She has written several books, including *Creating Writers–Linking Writing Assessment and Instruction* (Longman), and is a former language arts teacher, journalist, technical writer, consultant, and scoring director for dozens of state, county, and district writing assessments.

Jeff Hicks

Jeff Hicks has over 17 years of teaching experience in grades two through nine. Until recently, Jeff taught seventh/eighth grade English and math on a two-person teaching team, focusing on the reading/writing connection through six-trait writing activities. Currently, Jeff is a full-time writer and presenter.

Design/Production: Bill Westwood/Andy Cox, David Drury

Illustration: Jim Higgins, Mark DaGrossa, Scott Van Buren, Chris Vallo

Proofreading/Editorial: Erik Martin/Judy Bernheim, Alex Culpepper

Cover: Illustration by Claude Martinot Design

Printed in the United States of America

International Standard Book Number: 978-0-669-49037-4
International Standard Book Number: 0-669-49037-7
10 -PO- 10 09 08

Contents

Unit 4: Word Choice

Unit 5: Sentence Fluency

Unit 6: Conventions

name: .... date: ....

Warm-up Activity 1

"What Is a Trait?"

A *trait* is a characteristic or quality. For example, the traits of a good restaurant might be friendly service, good food, fair prices, and so on.

Write the traits of the items on this list.

- A good pet ______________________________
- A good driver ___________________________
- Good weather ___________________________

Do you think you understand the word *trait* pretty well? Write the best definition you can right here:

____

____

Think about the books you have loved most in your life. What did you like about them? What is it about the writing that makes it so good? What qualities or characteristics did that writing have?

____

____

____

Warm-up Activity 2

Ranking Three Papers

Read the three pieces of writing that follow. Decide which piece is strongest, which piece is next strongest, and which piece is weakest. All three papers describe the writer's hometown, Pinewood.

Sample 1

My home town is pretty neat. It has wide streets and some stores and houses. It is hot in the summer, but you can go swimming. I like it here because I have lots of friends. I have a dog, too. We do lots of stuff together. In the summer, I mostly go swimming or just do stuff with my friends.

Sample 2

I would not trade my home in Pinewood for anything. We have freezing cold winters with huge banks of snow to jump in. In the fall, carved pumpkins with scary faces and candles flickering inside show up on every front porch. In the spring, all the fields fill with daisies. In the summer, the streets are lined with gigantic maples that form a shady canopy you can walk under. Pinewood is special all year long. It is the place I will always call home.

Sample 3

Lots of people love the city, but I love Pinewood. It is fun in the winter because you can play in the snow, but it is fun in the summer, too. There are flowers and trees everywhere and the people are very friendly. You can go fishing in the Hawk River or swimming at the pool. My sister is the lifeguard there. She is not that nice to my friends, but it's kind of neat having a sister for a lifeguard.

Share Your Thoughts

Fill in each blank with the number of the sample (1, 2, or 3) that fits best. Be sure to add your reasons.

The strongest example is Sample ___ because

____

The next strongest is Sample ___ because

____

The weakest example is Sample ___ because

____

It's easy to imagine that writers just sit down and start writing. Maybe their heads are so full of ideas that the ideas just flow onto the paper. The truth is, though, that most writers do a lot of planning. In fact, planning is critical to almost everything we do.

Imagine a builder working without plans. Maybe one wall of a house would be taller than all the others. Maybe the builder would forget to put in the windows, or perhaps none of the doors would fit. Writing is much the same way. The better the plan, the more clearly your ideas come through.

This unit is about planning your writing so that your ideas interest your reader. You'll learn about

- prewriting with a list of details
- focusing on a main idea
- choosing interesting details
- taking out unnecessary details, or filler

Lesson 1

name: .... date: ....

Getting Started

***P**rewriting* **is what you do before you write to help organize, plan, or visualize your idea. It's like making out a shopping list before going to the grocery store. A grocery list helps you remember things you might otherwise forget. Also, if you follow your list, you won't find yourself buying a lot of things you don't need. Creating a *list* of details about your topic is one good way to prewrite. A list helps you remember details that you don't want to leave out. It also keeps you focused, so you don't fill your paper with unnecessary details—the way some people load their shopping carts with unnecessary items.**

A Three-Part List: Building Images

This writer chose "Adventures at the Rockpile" as his topic. To get started, he made a list in three parts: **Who, Where,** and (What We Were) **Doing.** Sometimes, he put an item on the list and then added a small detail to create a clearer image for the reader.

name: .... date: ....

Adventures at the Rockpile		
Who + Detail	**Where + Detail**	**Doing + Detail**
brother—Sam, 12 years old me—10 years old	rockpile—wooded area around old gravel pit	hiking—muddy trails, rocky hill, deer tracks
me—green rubber boots, raincoat	giant mud puddle	making stick "boats"
Sam—shorts, even in the rain; no coat	behind tree—thick bark	throwing pine cones to sink the boats
Sam and me	top of rocky hill—see over the trees	looking for our house

Use the List

Do you see any details on the list that you think this writer should include in his story? Circle them.

Now, let's see how the writer actually used information from the list to create a paragraph that helps you picture his "Adventures at the Rockpile." As you read, keep looking back at the list. Put a check next to each detail he included.

Adventures at the Rockpile

We have always called it the Rockpile. My older brother Sam may have been the one to call it that first. It's really a rocky hill that sticks up behind this old gravel pit, not far from our house. All kinds of trees have grown up around the area where they used to dig out big rocks and crush them into gravel. I don't think anyone put in the trails. They just sort of got that way from people walking and riding bikes and maybe from the deer who live there. We always see deer tracks when we hike, especially after it rains and the ground is soft. Sam and I like to go there when it's raining because of the huge puddles that cover parts of the trails. I like to splash in them and make a navy of stick boats. I always stay dry in my boots and raincoat. Sam always wears shorts and tennis shoes, so he never goes in the puddles. He just hides behind trees, throwing pine cones at my boats. We always end our adventures by climbing to the top of the hill and looking for the roof of our house. I've never seen it, but Sam says he can see it every time. I just go along with him so we won't argue, and he'll keep going on adventures with me.

name: ______________________ date: ____________

Was Anything Left Out?

This writer tells a good story. He includes many interesting details. Is there any important item from the list that the writer left out? ____ No ____ Yes

Did he include some important details that were not even on the list? ____ No ____ Yes

Write your thoughts about the "Rockpile" paragraph here:

____

____

____

Read the paragraph again. Underline any details that help you see or experience the writer's adventure in your mind.

Choosing a Topic for Writing

Choose one of the following topics to write about, or make up a topic of your own.

- My "adventure" place
- An interesting time with my brother or sister
- A rainy-day experience
- My grandparents' house
- A different topic ______________________

Make a Prewriting List

When you have chosen your topic, make a list like the one the "Rockpile" writer made. Think about the people you will write about, the place you want to tell the reader about, and the things you picture your characters doing. For each item, add a detail (an extra bit of information) that will paint a picture in the reader's mind.

name: .... date: ....

Who + Detail	Where + Detail	Doing + Detail

Starting Your Paragraph

As you begin to write, use as many details from your list as you can. Each time you use something from the list, put a check mark next to it. Use the list to visualize what you are writing about. Try to see the place in your mind as you write.

A Writer's Question

As you write, you may think of details that are not on your list—just as you might see an item at the grocery store that you forgot to put on your shopping list. Is it a good idea to add that detail to your writing, or should you stick to your list?

Lesson 2

name: .... date: ....

What's Your Point?

Have you ever talked to someone who seemed to talk on and on without ever coming to the point? You might find yourself thinking, "What in the world are you trying to say?" It's easy to get confused or frustrated when this happens. Some writers make the same mistake. They float from topic to topic like butterflies, never really settling on one main idea. Quality writing always has a clear main idea. When readers know what your main idea is, they understand how all the details fit.

Finding the Main Idea

Read Sample 1. Ask yourself, "What is the main idea?"

Hint: Is it possible that this writer doesn't have a main idea yet?

Sample 1

The very best thing about birthdays is getting to be with your family and having cake. I like my birthday cake to have at least two layers. I don't really get to eat a lot of cake except on my birthday or if someone is getting married and my family is invited. Cakes look best with candles. I like going to weddings, because there is usually a whole lot of good food that you can eat before they serve cake. I like the part of the wedding where you get to throw rice on the married couple. I went to this one wedding where we threw birdseed instead of rice. They said it was better for the environment, which is a good thing. I want the environment to be healthy for a long time, so when I have children they will have a clean world.

What Do You Think?

Is there a main idea in this paragraph? ____ Yes ____ No

Explain your answer.

____

____

Now read Sample 2, comparing it to Sample 1. What is this writer's main idea?

Sample 2

Have you ever been in a wedding? I have—three times. Being in weddings isn't too bad except for the clothes you have to wear. You see, I have two older sisters and one older brother. When I say older, I mean a lot older. I'm eleven and they're all in their twenties, and they are all married. I was in my first wedding three years ago, for my sister Laurie. I was only eight, so they thought I would make a cute ring bearer. I had to wear a tuxedo, and everyone said I looked "cute." Who wants to look cute? The year after that, I was a candle lighter in my brother Roger's wedding. I was too tall to be a cute ring bearer again, but I still had to wear a tuxedo. Do you know how uncomfortable those things are? Then last year, my sister Leslie got married. This time I got to be an usher and lead people to their seats. Yes, you guessed it, another tuxedo. If it weren't for the gifts the bride and groom give to the people in the wedding, I wouldn't put up with all that tuxedo wearing.

name: ______________________ date: ______________

What Do You Think?

Did you find a main idea for Sample 2? ____ Yes ____ No

If you said YES, underline the sentence that you think comes closest to giving you the writer's main idea.

Legs to Stand On

One way to see whether you have found a main idea is to picture your writing as a table. The main idea is like the tabletop, and the legs are the details that support it. Take away the details one by one, and the table gets a little wobbly. Take away all the legs, and the table crashes to the floor.

Strong Legs ⟶ Strong Table

On page 15, you will use a table sketch as a form of prewriting. First, choose one of the topics from the list, or come up with one of your own. Then put your main idea on the tabletop. Put details on the legs. Add more details if you need to; your table can have more than four legs.

name: .... date: ....

- My birthday party
- A wedding experience
- My favorite dessert
- Being the youngest/middle/oldest/only child
- A different topic idea ______________________

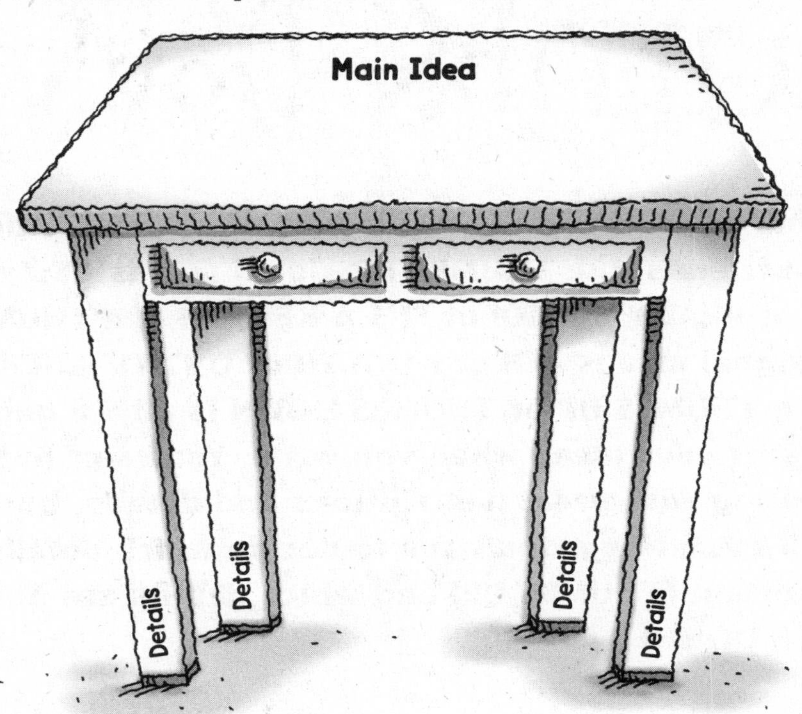

Writing from the Table

Now, use the main idea and supporting details from your table to write a short paragraph. It should be at least six sentences long. Some details on the legs might need more than one sentence to explain them. Use a separate piece of paper.

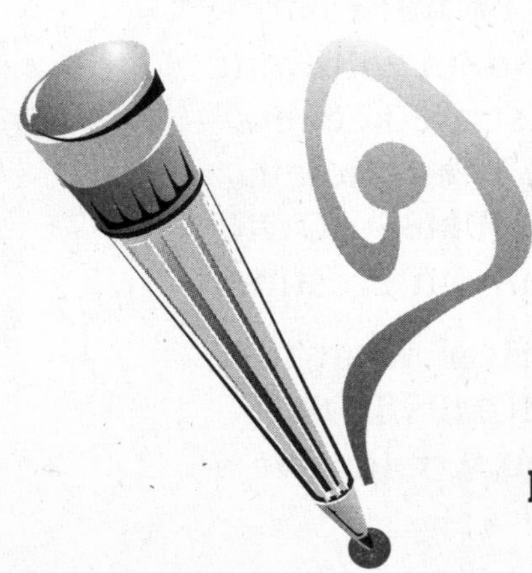

A Writer's Question

Did using your table sketch help you stay focused on your main idea? To find out, read your paragraph aloud to a partner. As you read, can your partner hear the main idea you had in mind?

Lesson 3

name: .... date: ....

Thumbs Up, Thumbs Down

Whether it's a movie review or part of a secret code between friends, the THUMBS UP signal means YES! or GREAT! or READY TO GO! or IT'S A KEEPER! The THUMBS DOWN signal means NO! or NO WAY! or OUT OF LUCK! Thinking THUMBS UP or THUMBS DOWN is also a quick way to sort your ideas when you write. You want to fill your writing with great descriptions and details, but you can't tell *everything*. You have to decide which details are important (THUMBS UP) and which details are not. (THUMBS DOWN)

Sorting It Out: THUMBS UP or DOWN?

Here is a list of informative details about the Middle Eastern country of Saudi Arabia. You may have visited this country or read about it previously, but do not worry if you have not.

Imagine that you are writing about Saudi Arabia and you want to fascinate your readers. Your purpose is to be informative and to tell about the country so that your readers will want to know more. Some of the details on your list are keepers—things your readers will really want to know. These details get a THUMBS UP! Some of the details get a THUMBS DOWN! These items are not important or not especially interesting.

As you read the list carefully, decide, as a writer, what to keep (THUMBS UP!) and what to toss out. (THUMBS DOWN!) Circle the number of each detail to which you would give a THUMBS UP!

name: .... date: ....

Details About Saudi Arabia

1. Riyadh is the capital city.
2. The country covers 865,000 square miles.
3. Saudi Arabia is the world's 12th largest country.
4. The Red Sea forms most of the eastern border.
5. The unit of money is called the *riyal.*
6. Southeastern Saudi Arabia is covered by a sandy desert called the *Rub' al-Khali.*
7. There are mountains in Saudi Arabia.
8. Soccer is the country's most popular sport.
9. A desert is a dry, sandy area that does not get much rain.
10. Cats are popular pets in Saudi Arabia.
11. Lots of people all over the world like cats.
12. Women in Saudi Arabia wear clothes that cover their heads and bodies.
13. The language of Saudi Arabia is Arabic.
14. Not many people in the United States speak Arabic.
15. There is a sword on the Saudi Arabian flag.
16. The Saudi Arabian flag is green.
17. The United States flag is red, white, and blue.
18. Boys and girls go to separate schools.
19. School is important no matter where you live.
20. It is not polite in Saudi Arabia to drink more than two cups of coffee.
21. Coffee is made from coffee beans.
22. The State of Oregon is not as large as Saudi Arabia.

Compare Lists

Circle the details that you think are most interesting. Then compare your list with that of a partner. Did you both give the same items a THUMBS UP? If you did not, take a few minutes to discuss why you circled the items you did. How many items did you choose?

Using the THUMBS UP! to Write

Look again at the items you circled. Use them in a paragraph about Saudi Arabia. Remember: Do not worry if you did not know much about Saudi Arabia before. Just work from your list of details. Use at least six THUMBS UP! items from your list.

name: .... date: ....

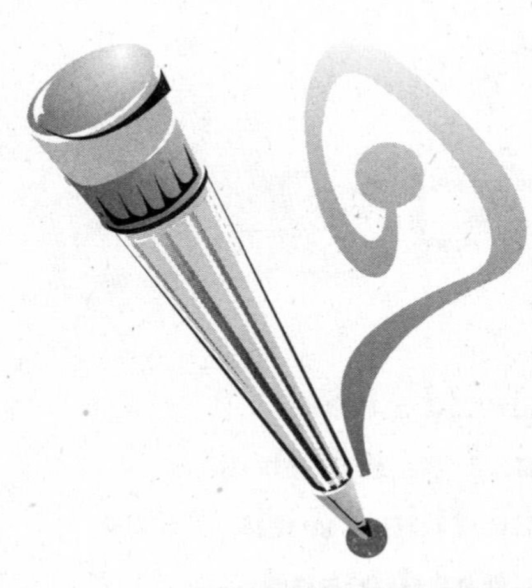

A Writer's Question

Just because you want to tell everything about your topic does not mean your reader wants to read everything! How skilled are you at sorting out the THUMBS UP from the THUMBS DOWN details? Rate yourself from 1 to 6, with 1 low, and 6 very high.

1	2	3	4	5	6
I'm *still* not sure what to keep.					I'll give my sorting skills a big THUMBS UP!

Lesson 4

name: .... date: ....

Unpacking to Stay in Focus

When you pack for a trip, you have to decide how much to bring. You don't want that suitcase to weigh a ton! You also don't want your writing to be filled with unnecessary details. Pick a topic you can handle and "pack light," tossing out the details you do not need. When you first write, *everything* looks good. You don't want to toss out a thing. But if you can leave your writing for a day or two—or even longer—you may be surprised when you come back to find that many details no longer seem important.

Sharing an Example: Dovey Coe

Read this sample from writer Frances O'Roark Dowell. Notice how Dowell's character, Dovey, a twelve-year-old country girl, tells you a lot about her life without telling you too much.

Besides Caroline, I got me an older brother named Amos, age of thirteen, and he loves good adventure as much as I do. We spend a good portion of our days running around on Katie's Knob, hunting arrowheads or hunks of crystal quartz, tracking all manner of wild animals and generally having a good time.

We live in the house my daddy grew up in, and every morning I look out upon the same mountains my daddy looked out upon when he was a child. I like sitting on the porch watching the summer evenings fall across the valley,

name: .... date: ....

listening to Daddy pick old tunes on his guitar. I enjoy the cozy feel of sitting next to the woodstove when there's a frosty bite in the air.

There's at least a million other things that all add up to my good life here, more things than I can say or even remember, they're so natural to me now.

That's why it's hard to believe they might send me away from here.

Frances O'Roark Dowell, *Dovey Coe* (New York: Atheneum, 2000) pp. 4–5

What Did You Find Out?

Dovey stays focused on one topic: her life in the country. In the left circle, write several details that you know about her life in the country. In the right circle, jot down information that Dovey does not tell you, things that you probably do not need to know anyway—for instance, how tall she is.

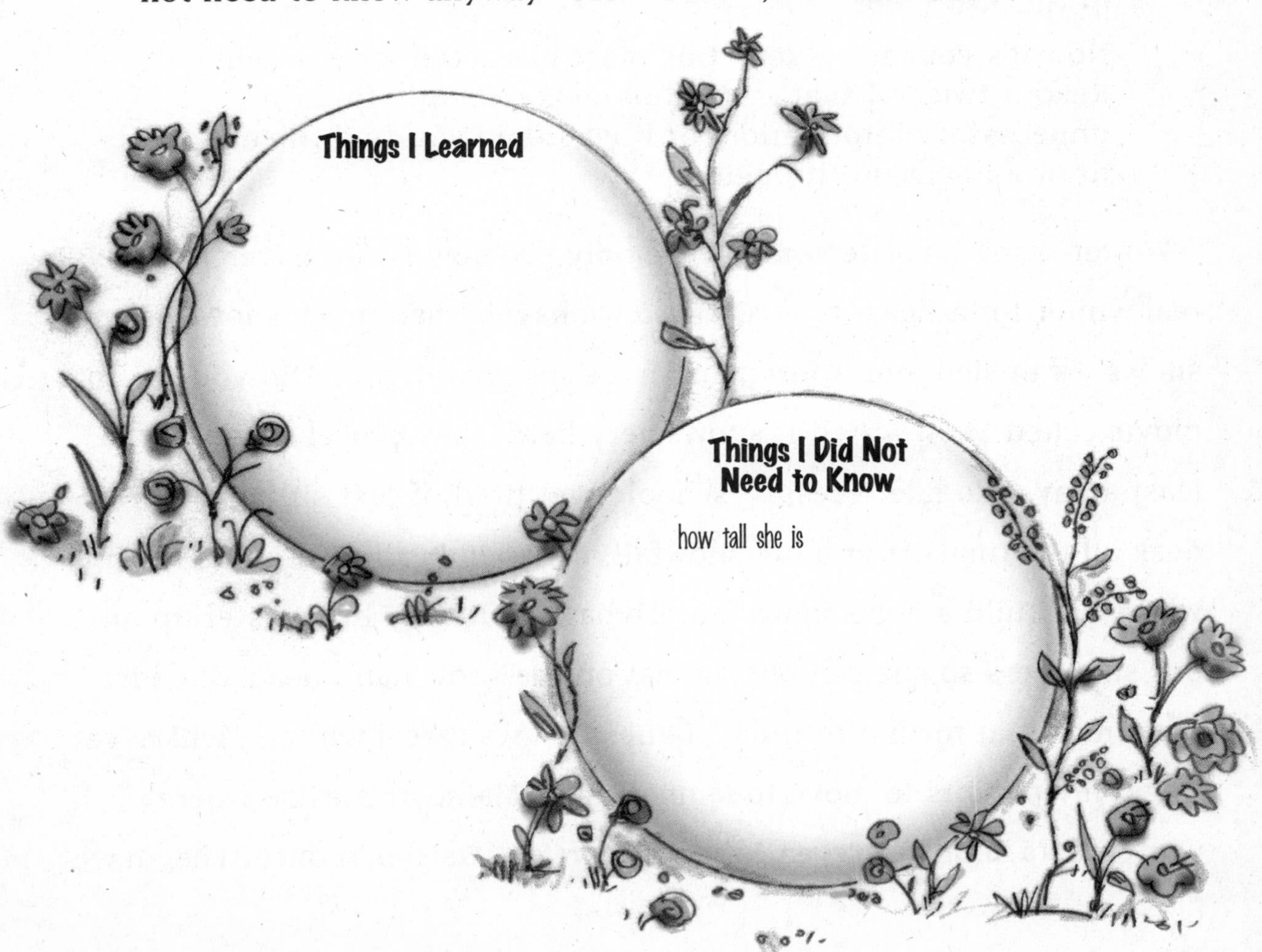

What If?

What if Dovey told you everything about her life? Extra details would only take up space Dovey could be using to tell you something new and interesting. "Filler" weighs down your writing. The good news is that it's easy to get rid of filler. You just draw a line right through it.

Nico was willing to do almost any job to earn money for a new bike. He mowed the lawn, cleaned the garage, and washed the car. ~~Nico got thirsty when he worked.~~ He even walked the neighbor's dogs, though both of them were hard to handle.

Finding the Filler

Now it's your turn. Read this piece about winter weather. Read it twice, if that is helpful. Look carefully for any unnecessary information, or filler. When you find filler, draw a line right through it.

Winter is my favorite season. The only problem is, we haven't had a real winter for at least two years, so we haven't had much snow. When it snows, I can sled, build forts, and have snowball fights. Did you see that movie called *Snowday?* If it snows very hard, they cancel school for at least a day. I do like recess at school. I get tired of just sitting at my desk all the time. After a big snowfall, my friends all meet in my yard, where we build a huge snowman. We have to lift my little sister up on our shoulders so she can put the hat on the snowman's head. She just got a new coat for her birthday. I guess if I want real winter, I will have to get my parents to move to Minnesota or Maine or Alaska, where winter lasts almost forever. I did a report on Wisconsin once. They have

name: .... date: ....

pretty cold winters, and they make a lot of cheese there. I love cheese.

Share and Compare

How much filler did you cross out?

____ A lot!

____ Some, but I kept most things.

____ None. I didn't cross out anything.

When you have finished, compare your revised version with your partner's. Did you cross out the same things? If not, discuss why you decided to cross out the things you did.

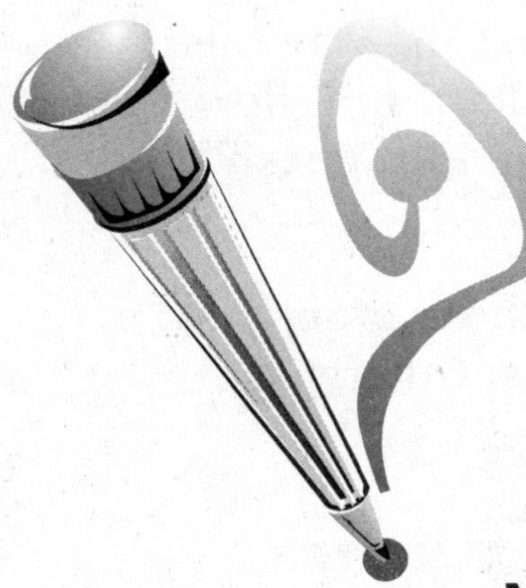

A Writer's Question

Can you find any filler in your writing? Now that you have had some practice, look for filler in a piece of your writing. First write out your main idea, and then write one example of filler.

My main idea: ______________________________

One example of filler: ______________________________

____

____

____

____

Unit 2

Organization

Have you ever read something and said to yourself, "I'm just not following this at all!"? Perhaps you were daydreaming or thinking of something else. That happens to all readers. Sometimes, though, it's not you at all. Sometimes it's just the way the information is written. It might be hard to follow. The writing may not be clear, or one idea doesn't seem to go with the next idea.

Good organization can help solve these problems. Writers need to organize their ideas. Otherwise, readers feel lost or confused.

In this unit, you'll find ways to organize your writing to make sure that your reader understands it. You'll learn about

- writing a strong lead
- learning three patterns for organizing information
- using the right pattern for the right purpose
- wrapping up with a strong conclusion

name: .... date: ....

Writing a Strong Lead

In the game of baseball, the leadoff batter's job is to make something happen by hitting the ball or somehow getting on base. Leadoff batters don't have to hit home runs, but they do want to get the game going for the team. Writers try to do much the same thing by stirring the reader's interest with their leadoff sentences. Of course, the very first lead a writer writes isn't always the best one. In fact, writers often create several different leads and then choose the one that will make readers want to keep reading. In this lesson, you are going to practice choosing the best lead for different kinds of writing. Then try writing a lead of your own.

Sharing an Example: The Bad Beginning

Read the lead on page 26. Ask yourself how it makes you feel: Curious? A little nervous? Does it make you want to read more?

If you are interested in stories with happy endings, you would be better off reading some other book. In this book, not only is there no happy ending, there is no happy beginning and very few happy things in the middle. This is because not very many happy things happened in the lives of the three Baudelaire youngsters. Violet, Klaus, and Sunny Baudelaire were intelligent children, and they were charming, and resourceful, and had pleasant facial features, but they were extremely unlucky, and most everything that happened to them was rife with misfortune, misery, and despair. I'm sorry to tell you this, but that is how the story goes.

Lemony Snicket, *The Bad Beginning* (New York: Harpertrophy, 1999), p. 1

The author, Lemony Snicket, has tried a very interesting strategy. His lead is telling you not to read his book. What do you think of this lead? Write your reaction here:

Choosing a Winner

Now, it's time to make some choices. Following are two possible leads for two different stories. One story is about a wolf, and the other story is about pioneers. In each case, read both leads and then decide whether lead A or lead B would work better. Mark your answer and explain your choice.

Two possible leads for a story about a wolf

A The full, yellow moon finally poked through the thick clouds. Mantak, a young female wolf, raised her head to the night sky and began to howl. Her lonely voice echoed through the trees, but no other wolves picked up her song. For the first time in her life, Mantak was totally alone.

B Her name was Mantak, and she was a wolf. There was a full moon. She howled at the moon, in the forest, all by herself. Mantak looked pretty scared and sad.

name: .... date: ....

Lead **A** or Lead **B?** ____ Why?

____

____

____

____

Two possible leads for a report on Oregon Trail pioneers

A This is a report about people who moved west to find new land. They moved west on the Oregon Trail in covered wagons. They were the pioneers. I will tell you about them.

B What was it that pulled the pioneers west along the Oregon Trail? The spirit of adventure? A sense of freedom? I think it was the land, a magnetic force that pulled these people west in their bouncing covered wagons.

Lead **A** or Lead **B?** ____ Why?

____

____

____

____

Share and Compare

With a partner, compare the leads each of you selected. Did you make the same choices? Why?

Your Turn at Bat

You have looked at a lead from a published author and practiced choosing a lead from two possibilities. What's next? Writing your own leads, of course!

Take a close look at the list of writing topics on page 28 and choose one, or use a topic of your own.

Moving
A wild animal
An adventure at night
How it feels to be lost

Another topic ______________________________

One of your leads needs to be as strong as you can write it. Make your reader want to keep reading. The other lead should be weak. Maybe it's boring or it just announces what you will be talking about. Look back at the examples you read earlier to remind yourself how strong and weak leads sound.

Lead 1

____

____

Lead 2

____

____

Share and Compare

When you have finished, meet with a partner and read your leads aloud. Can you tell which one is your partner's strong lead? Can your partner pick out your strong lead?

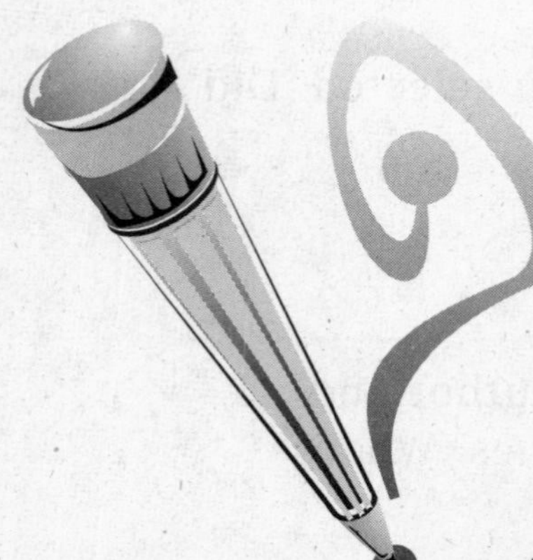

A Writer's Question

When you read a book, do you notice the lead? Look at a book that you read recently and liked. Read the lead aloud to a friend. What do you think? Is it strong or weak?

Book Title: ______________________________

Author: ______________________________

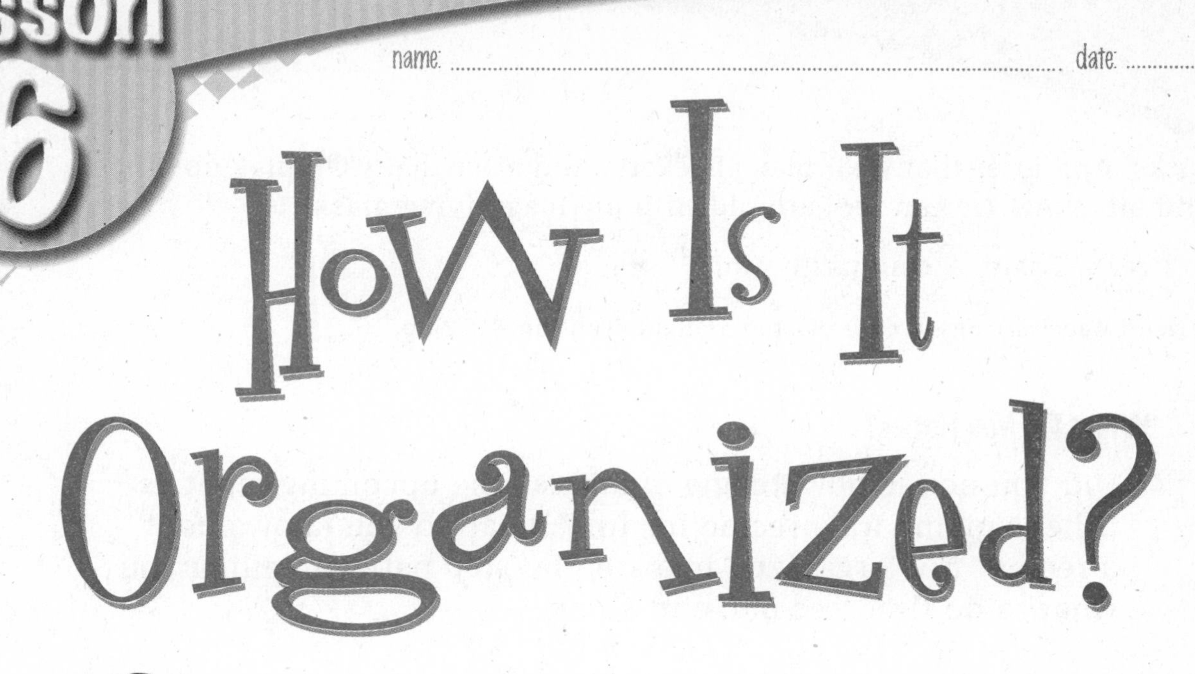

name: .... date: ....

Suppose you are moving into a new house, and you need to organize your furniture. How about putting the refrigerator in the bathroom? Or the couch on the roof? The bed could go in the kitchen. . . . Well, you can see that bad organization could make your house very hard to live in. Writers face the same situation when they decide how to organize ideas on paper. They know they cannot put details just anywhere. Weak organization makes writing very hard to read. In this lesson, you will learn three organizational patterns, see how each might look in a paragraph, and then imitate one of those three patterns.

Sharing an Example: Ira Sleeps Over

If you were going to have a friend spend the night, your friend might ask, "What are we going to do?" That's exactly what happens in the book *Ira Sleeps Over.* Read Reggie's response to Ira. Think about how Reggie organizes his answer.

"Tonight," he said, "when you come to my house, we are going to have fun, fun, fun. First, I'll show you my junk collection. And after that we'll have a wrestling match. And after that, a pillow fight. And after that we'll do magic tricks. And after that we'll play checkers. And after that we'll play dominoes. And after that we can fool around with my magnifying glass."

"Great!" I said. "I can hardly wait."

Bernard Waber, *Ira Sleeps Over* (Boston: Houghton Mifflin, 1972), p. 16

What Did You Notice?

Did you notice how Reggie organizes the upcoming night as if he is giving Ira a recipe for fun? What do you know about a recipe? It is organized in a step-by-step pattern, telling you what to do first, second, and so on.

Three Organizational Patterns

Here are three ways to organize information. Read each one carefully.

A) Step-by-Step

This is a great pattern for showing someone *how* to do something, such as make cookies or ride a bike. Give your reader one step at a time, making sure the steps are in order. The order is very important!

B) Comparison-Contrast

Here is an excellent way to organize information when you want to show how things are alike or different: How were wooly mammoths like modern elephants? How were they different? When you answer these two questions, you are comparing and contrasting.

C) Most Important to Least Important

You can't always tell *everything* about a topic, especially if you don't have a lot of space. A good solution is to start with the most important information, add the second most important information, and continue until you have used all the available space.

name: .... date: ....

Naming the Pattern

Here are three paragraphs, each using one of the organizational patterns you just read about. As you read each paragraph, decide which pattern is being used. Put the letter of your choice on the line:

A Step-by-Step

B Comparison-Contrast

C Most Important to Least Important

Sample 1

When it comes time to vote for class president, Susan should be your choice. The most important thing about Susan is that she is a great listener. She will listen to your concerns. Another of Susan's strengths is that she is very energetic. She will use her energy to get any job done. Susan is organized, too. You can tell by looking at her desk. Vote for Susan for class president!

Organizational Pattern ____

Sample 2

The first thing to do when it is time to change a light bulb is to make sure the lamp is unplugged. You don't want to risk being electrocuted! Next, give the bulb time to cool off. Once it is cool, carefully turn the bulb to the left. Remember, righty-tighty, lefty-loosey. Turn until the bulb comes out, and then throw the old bulb away, being careful not to break it. Replace the old bulb with a new one of the same type.

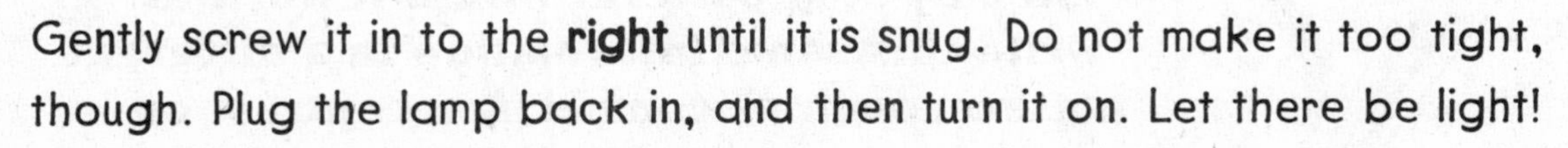

Gently screw it in to the **right** until it is snug. Do not make it too tight, though. Plug the lamp back in, and then turn it on. Let there be light!

Organizational Pattern ____

name: ____________________ date: __________

Sample 3

Though they look very different, a helicopter and an airplane are both able to fly through the air. A helicopter uses whirling blades or rotors, but an airplane uses wings for flight. Rotors and wings look very much alike. However, these two aircraft move in slightly different ways. A helicopter can fly forward, backward, or sideways. It can even hover. Most airplanes can't move sideways or hover.

Organizational Pattern ____

Imitating a Pattern

Choose one pattern to use in a short paragraph (five sentences or more). Choose your own topic. For instance, if you choose the pattern in Sample 2, explain how to do something other than change a light bulb.

____

____

____

____

____

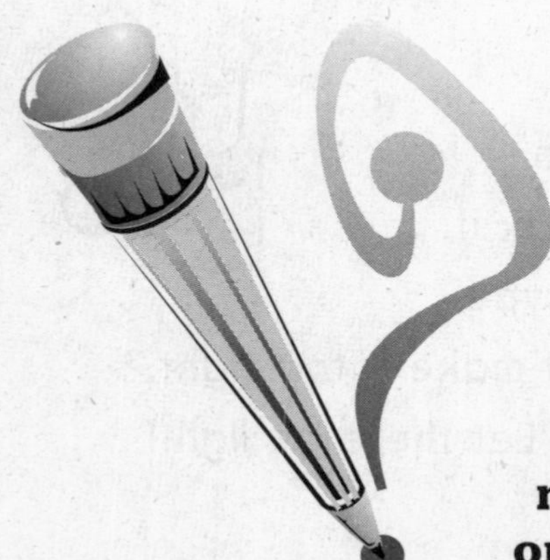

A Writer's Question

We can probably agree that "How to Change a Light Bulb" is written in a step-by-step pattern. Would it work to write this same information in a different pattern, such as comparison-contrast or most important to least important? Why or why not?

name: .... date: ....

Matching the Pattern to the Task

If you were going to tell a friend about a great movie you had just seen, how would you do it? Would you start at the beginning and then tell the whole story? Would you compare it to another movie you have both seen? Would you pick out some key things to share—such as who was in the movie or what kind of movie it was? Writers have to think about organizing ideas for their audience. Giving readers the right information at the right time makes the message clear and appealing to read.

Six Patterns: Organizing Your Writing

In Lesson 6, we looked at three organizational patterns. In this lesson, we will review those patterns and look at three more. Read the descriptions carefully. Think about any writing you have done (or writing you have read) that used one of these patterns. Later, you will use this list to match organizational patterns with various writing tasks.

name: .... date: ....

Six Organizational Patterns

Step-by-Step

This is the pattern to use if you want to show someone how to do something, such as making cookies or riding a bike. You show the reader, step-by-step, exactly what to do.

Comparison and Contrast

Here is an excellent way to organize information when you want to show how things are alike or different. For example, how are lions like tigers? Describing two different people, things, or ideas is a good way to make comparisons.

Most Important to Least Important

You don't always have enough space to tell everything. Sometimes it's a good strategy to begin with what is most important, then say what is next most important, and continue until you have filled the available space.

Main Idea and Support

When you are focusing on one big point, this is the pattern to use. State your main idea clearly. Then frame it with supporting details that help the reader understand the point you wish to make.

Chronological Retelling of Events

Using chronological, or time, order (what happened first, second, next, and so on) can be a great way to tell a story or tell about the history of an event or a place.

Key Points

Rather than telling everything about a person, place, or event, imagine the three or four key questions a curious reader might ask about your topic. Answer those in your writing. This process keeps your ideas focused.

name: .... date: ....

Playing Matchmaker

For this part of the lesson, work with a partner. Together you will look at a list of writing tasks and then select the organizational pattern that is the best match for each task. Talk about each one. Then write your answer, using the letters A through F.

Six Writing Tasks

Brochure on things to do at an amusement park

Organizational Pattern ____

Description of how to set up a tent

Organizational Pattern ____

A history of your town—how it began, how it has changed

Organizational Pattern ____

An article on how having a dog for a pet is different from having a cat for a pet

Organizational Pattern ____

A newspaper story about a bank robbery

Organizational Pattern ____

An opinion paper on why recess should be ten minutes longer

Organizational Pattern ____

Compare with the Class

For each writing task, be ready to explain why you and your partner made the choice you did. Is it possible to have more than one "right" answer for some of these writing tasks? How could that be?

name: .... date: ....

Using a Pattern

Write a short paragraph explaining to your readers why they should buy ________________________.
(Fill in the blank to suit yourself—a type of food, an appliance, a game, a toy, a pet—anything.) Before you begin writing, choose the organizational pattern that you think will work for your topic.

Organizational pattern I will use: ________________

Write your paragraph here. It should be at least five sentences long.

____

____

____

____

____

____

____

____

____

____

____

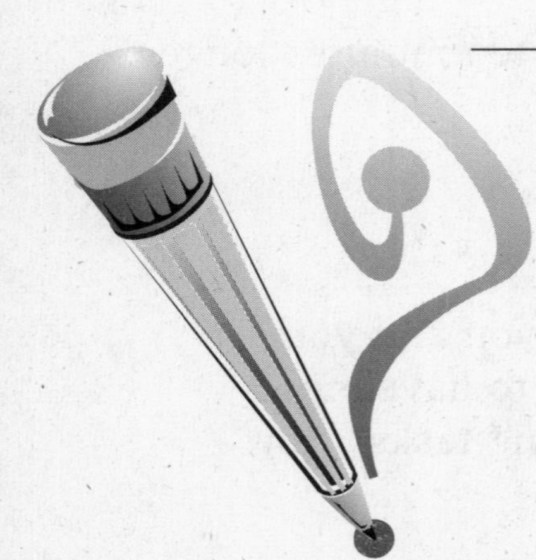

A Writer's Question

Which organizational pattern do you feel most comfortable using?

Which pattern do you feel least comfortable using?

Lesson 8

name: .... date: ....

Wrapping It Up

You've heard of stories with surprise endings. And you may have read stories in which the reader is left to decide how things turn out. You've also read endings where everyone lives happily ever after. Whatever type of ending the writer chooses, it needs to put the right finishing touch on everything the writer has written up to that point. It needs to wrap things up.

Sharing an Example: Shiloh

A good ending has a sound and a feel that clearly tells the reader that the story or essay is over. It's like sensing when it's time to say goodbye when you're talking on the phone to a friend. Here is an example from the Newbery-award-winning book *Shiloh.* Notice how these sentences signal that the author is wrapping up.

I look at the dark closing in, sky getting more and more purple, and I'm thinking how nothing is as simple as you guess—not right or wrong, not Judd Travers, not even me or this dog I got here. But the good part is I saved Shiloh and opened my eyes some. Now that ain't bad for eleven.

Phyllis Reynolds Naylor, *Shiloh* (New York: Atheneum, 1991), p. 144

What do think about the ending on page 37? Does it sound as if the writer is wrapping up? Write your thoughts here.

Select an Ending: Mantak

Read the short passage from a story called "Mantak" and three possible ways to end it. Decide which ending best wraps up the story, and circle the number of your choice.

The full, yellow moon finally poked through the thick clouds. Mantak, a young female wolf, raised her head to the night sky and began to howl. Her lonely voice echoed through the trees, but no other wolves picked up her sad song. For the first time in her life, Mantak was totally alone. Where was the pack? Where were her brothers and sisters? Her howls seemed to ask the questions. Mantak tried to clear her head of the fearful thoughts that were trying to creep inside. Go back to the beginning, she told herself. The whole pack had been on a hunt, chasing an injured bull moose up the hillside from the river. Mantak had kept to the back of the group, with the other young wolves, when suddenly the moose made a desperate turn to try to make it back to the river. She had tried to slip to the side, behind a tree, but one of the moose's flailing hooves caught her on the side of the head, knocking her down and out. When she woke up, Mantak found herself in a hollow of snow at the base of a large tree. Her head still hurt, but the pain told her she was alive.

name: ________________ date: ________

Possible Endings

1. Mantak knew she would never find her family. She bravely began to search for a new pack to join, though she knew it would not be the same. She had learned a great deal from this experience and would always be wary of a moose's sharp hooves.

2. Mantak filled her nostrils with the crisp evening air. A familiar scent, a trace of her family, was still lingering. If she was going to make it back to the pack, she would have to follow her nose. She would have to be strong and live up to the name her father had given her, Mantak: Ruler of the night.

3. There was still blood from her wound. Now she would be hunted, so she hid in a cave but there was a bear there. They became friends. The End.

What's Your Choice?

Which ending sounds best? Read it aloud to a partner. Explain why you think your ending works better than the others do.

I chose ending ____ because ______________________________

____

Your Turn to Write

"Take Me to Your Leader" is about a kid who loves space and thinks that UFOs or aliens could be real. Read the passage carefully. Then write an ending that fits the story and wraps it up well.

Take Me to Your Leader

Ever since I was four, I have loved to look up at the night sky. I live in the city, so it's not always easy to see the stars because of all the lights. On the roof of my building, there's an observation patio where I can at least be above most of the city lights. I got a telescope for my birthday, which takes me even farther into space. Every time I look through my telescope, I think, what if there's someone or something looking back at me? It could happen, so I want

name: .... date: ....

to be ready. Now, this is going to sound a little wacky, but I made a welcome sign with a smiley face and a peace sign and everything. I've had my sign for about a year, secretly of course, and nothing has ever happened during all that time. Then two nights ago, I got this weird tingling feeling and saw a flash of bright light.

Share and Compare

After you have finished writing, read the passage aloud, with your ending, to your partner. How does it sound? Did your partner's ending take the story in a different direction from the one your ending suggested?

A Writer's Question

Think of some books that you have read and liked. Read the conclusions. Are they well done? Record the titles of one or two books you think have really good endings—then compare your choices with those of a partner.

Every writer wants to create writing so good that readers forget everything else because they can't stop reading. That kind of writing has *voice.*

Voice isn't like salt or nutmeg. You can't just sprinkle it over your writing. Voice comes from within you. It's your personal energy put on paper. Your voice is who you are. The more of yourself you put into your writing, the more voice your writing will have.

This unit is about finding your own voice. You will learn about

- listening or reading for voice
- recognizing different characters' voices
- making your readers see and feel what is happening
- developing your own voice

name: .... date: ....

Help! I Need a Voice-Over!

Personal narrative writing is simply *you,* telling your stories and sharing your experiences. Because you are writing about your own life, your voice should be obvious in every word you write. Your audience will want to feel joy, frustration, embarrassment, pride, or any other emotion you felt. You can help them by filling your words with the energy of your experience. Writing that has this kind of voice sounds almost alive—it's electric! Writing that doesn't have this power is begging for an energy injection.

Ranking the Voice

Here are three short samples of personal narrative writing. Read them silently or aloud quietly to yourself. Keep your eyes and ears open for the voice, the energy that comes from each piece. Then, with a partner, rank the three narratives according to the amount of voice, or energy, each one has.

name: .... date: ....

Sample 1

Shooting Hoops

Whenever I have a spare moment, I love to shoot some hoops. I shoot before I go to school. I shoot at every recess. I shoot when I get home from school. I shoot hoops all day on the weekends. I even put a basketball in my backpack so that I can shoot hoops anywhere I go. Sure, it looks funny, but who cares? I am a hoop-shooting machine.

Sample 2

Baseball Cards

I started collecting baseball cards when I was four. I have been collecting them now for five years. I used to keep them in a shoe box. Now, I keep them in notebooks. I have all my most special cards in one notebook. The notebook is red. I would feel bad if my red notebook got lost or accidentally put in the garbage. It has my favorite cards.

Sample 3

My Cousin Maria

I don't know how she does it. I used to think she was just faking it—you know, putting on an act. But now I know it's for real. I'm talking about Maria's smile. Every time I see her, she's smiling one of those smiles that light up her whole face like a sunrise, and you can't help but smile back. Even on days when I don't really feel like doing any smiling (you should know that I am the original grouch—I could win a medal for it), she'll come rolling up in her wheelchair and torch me with a ball of sunlight. Wheelchair or not, she's the happiest person I know, and she makes me feel happy even when I'm not in the mood to be happy. I really don't know how she does it.

name: ______ date: ______

Voice Rankings

Write your rankings here by putting the title of each sample in the blank where you think it fits.

1 ______________ (strong voice, great energy)
2 ______________ (so-so voice, medium energy)
3 ______________ (weak voice, low energy)

Talk About the Voices

Get ready to share your own and your partner's rankings with those of the rest of the class. How do they compare? Remember that discussing involves talking *and* listening.

A Voice-Lift

The narratives ranked 2 and 3 are crying out for help—can you hear them? To do your part, choose one of the passages you ranked *weaker* in voice (2 or 3). Your job is to revise the narrative to strengthen the voice. Look for places where you think the author is holding back, parts where you know you should be feeling strong voice energy. Add some details, or change any words that will help give this piece the voice-lift it needs.

Sample ____ with my revisions:

____

____

____

____

____

____

____

Share and Compare

Share your revised writing with a partner. Did you make the same kinds of revisions? Did you have to make the exact same changes to strengthen the voice? Be ready to talk about the changes each of you made.

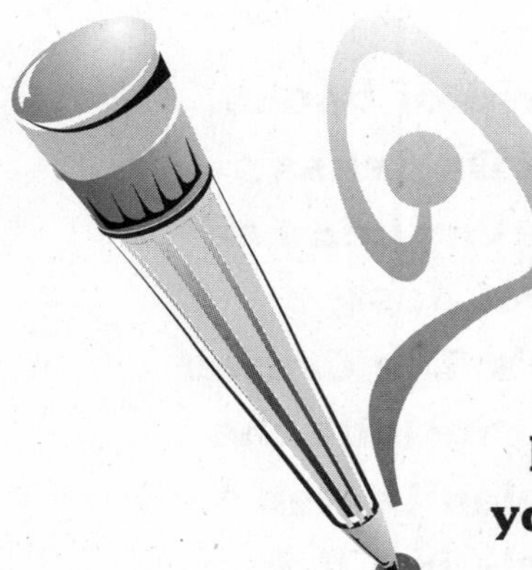

A Writer's Question

Finding voice in a piece of writing is a matter of looking and listening. What are you looking and listening for? Imagine you're giving advice to someone who doesn't know how to look or listen for voice. Write your advice here.

name: .... date: ....

Favorite Voices

So many memorable voices live in the world of books. Some are old favorites: the rhyming cat in Dr. Seuss's *The Cat in the Hat,* proud Mike Mulligan in Virginia Lee Burton's *Mike Mulligan and His Steam Shovel*, fast-talking Tucker the mouse in George Selden's *The Cricket in Times Square.* Favorite new voices might include the odd bird Tacky in *Tacky the Penguin,* by Helen Lester, and the confident voices of the farm animals in *Click-Clack-Moo, Cows That Type,* by Doreen Cronin. Sharing these voices is a way to help someone else find a new favorite voice and maybe a new favorite book. Hearing new and different voices will also enrich your writing.

Sharing an Example: Secret Letters from 0 to 10

Here is an example of voice from writer Susie Morgenstern. In her book, ten-year-old Ernest lives a ho-hum voiceless life until he meets Victoria, a ball of fire who helps Ernest discover the simple pleasures and wonders of the world around him.

Ernest didn't walk at his usual pace. He didn't run, either. He just followed Victoria.

He couldn't see the envy of the other girls, who were getting ready to attack Victoria. But Victoria did see them. She read the anonymous notes on her desk: "We knew him before you! Watch out!" "Watch it, you cow. Leave Ernest alone!"

She answered each note with the same patient explanation: "I love Ernest. That's all there is to it. We can't help it. And what is more, I understand him, and I want him to be happy. We're getting married in thirteen years, eight months, and three days. This is an invitation to our wedding."

Susie Morgenstern, *Secret Letters from 0 to 10* (New York: Viking, 1996) p. 35

What Did You Learn?

What kind of voices did you hear? How did they make you feel? What does Victoria's voice tell you about her? What do the voices of the notes tell about the people who wrote them?

A Voice That Stands Out

Think about books and stories you have read that really stand out in your mind. Do they stand out because of their strong voices? Find a favorite book to share. Skim through it to find a part you think is *really* strong in voice. Read the part aloud to yourself to make sure it's the one you want and that it is long enough to let the voice come through.

Share

In a small group, take turns reading your passages aloud. (Make sure you tell the title and author. Someone in your group may want to read the whole book!) Listen carefully so you can comment on the amount of voice, the kind of voice you hear (or don't hear), and how the author has created voice in each shared passage.

name: ______________________________ date: ______________

Trying Another Voice

To stretch yourself as a writer, it's important not only to hear different voices but also to imitate them as a way of practicing. Choose one of the voices you heard in your sharing groups. You may select the voice you shared, if you wish. You may also choose a voice in *Secret Letters from 0 to 10.* When you have chosen a voice to imitate, write a short paragraph of five to seven sentences. Choose your own topic, and do not copy the writer's words. Try to make your paragraph sound the way it would if the author you chose had written it. For example, Victoria's voice in *Secret Letters from 0 to 10* is confident. She loves Ernest no matter what the other girls say in their notes. You could imitate that voice by writing about something in a confident way.

name: .... date: ....

A Writer's Question

How did you feel about this way of practicing writing with voice? Read your paragraph aloud to your group, and share your thoughts. Then rate your feelings on the scale.

1	2	3	4	5	6
This was pretty hard. My own voice kept coming through.					This practice was fun. I like trying a new voice.

Lesson 11

name: .... date: ....

Pumping It Up!

Is a basketball without any air still a basketball? Without air, it won't bounce like a basketball. It won't pass or shoot like a basketball. Until it has air pumped inside, that piece of orange, bumpy rubber is flat and dull. Without voice, writing is flat and dull, too. But just as a basketball can be ready for action with a few pumps of air, so your writing can be revived with a few word changes, some details, and a little enthusiasm. Got your voice pump ready?

Sharing an Example: The Sign of the Beaver

There are many different kinds of voices: funny, sad, quiet, loud, confident, nervous, and so on. Before you look at some dull, voiceless writing, here is a passage from a book filled with voice. Where does the voice come from in this passage?

name: .... date: ....

Sample 1

He turned and looked back at the log house. It was a fair house, he thought; his mother would have no cause to be ashamed of it. He had helped to build every inch of it. He had helped to cut down the spruce trees and haul the logs and square and notch them. He had stood at one end of every log and raised it, one on top of the other, fitting the notched ends together as snugly as though they had grown that way. He had climbed the roof to fasten down the cedar splints with long poles, and dragged up pine boughs to cover them. Behind the cabin were the mounds of corn he had helped to plant, the green blades already shooting up, and the pumpkin vines just showing between the stumps of trees.

If only it were not so quiet. He had been alone before. His father had often gone into the forest to hunt, for hours on end. Even when he was there, he was not much of a talker. Sometimes they had worked side by side through a whole morning without his speaking a single word. But this silence was different. It coiled around Matt and reached into his stomach to settle there in a hard knot.

Elizabeth Speare, *The Sign of the Beaver* (Boston: Houghton Mifflin, 1983) pp. 1–2

What if we rewrote this passage but took out most of the voice? Read along as your teacher reads this voice-free version to you.

Sample 2

He turned and looked back at the log house. It was a fair house, he thought; his mother would have no cause to be ashamed of it.

If only it were not so quiet.

What Did You See? What Did You Feel?

To take out the voice, a lot of words had to be removed. Compare the "pictures" created by each sample. Then compare the feelings you had as you read each sample. Write your responses here.

In **Sample 1,** I can "see" ______________________________.

I can feel ______________________________.

In **Sample 2,** I can "see" ______________________________.

I can feel ______________________________.

Where Does Voice Come From?

You probably "saw" a clearer picture in Sample 1. You probably had stronger feelings as you read it, too. Why? The author shares her vision with you through the number and kinds of details she includes. Her voice energizes the details and descriptions. You can see the house Matt had helped to build. You can feel his pride about helping build the house, and you can sense his loneliness as he recalls his father and feels the silence slip around him. An important way to bring voice into your writing, then, is to use details to paint a picture and to help readers experience the same feelings the characters have.

Pumping Up the Voice: The Best Day of Summer

Here is a piece of lifeless writing. Revise it by pumping it full of voice. The voice you put into this writing needs to fit the topic and the purpose of the writing.

Hint: To revise this writing, think about adding the kinds of details that make feelings come alive for your reader.

I was really excited about going. It would be the best day of the summer. We were going to go rafting on the Snake River.

My mother, father, sister, and brother got to go. They were excited, too. My dad knew a lot of stuff about rafting. This would be neat.

When we got to the Snake River, it looked big. The water was moving fast. I got scared. It turned out to be fun. We ate sandwiches and drank soda pop. I wore a life jacket and got wet.

It was the best thing I did all summer.

Share and Compare

Share your revised version with a partner. What revisions did each of you make to pump up the voice? Did both of you create the same kind of voice?

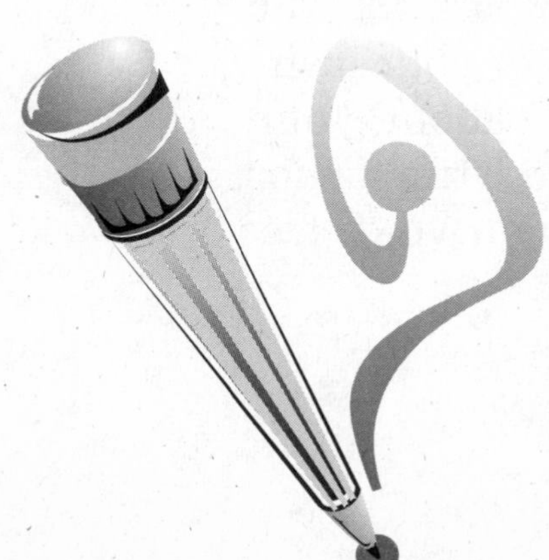

A Writer's Question

What words would describe the voice you created for "The Best Day of Summer"? Is this the voice you wanted to create?

Lesson 12

name: .... date: ....

Your World, Your Voice

Have you ever watched a movie with friends and then talked about it afterward? Even though you all watched the same movie, you probably didn't all remember it the same way. That's because you are all individuals. You may share some common experiences (like watching a movie together or going to the same school), but you all look at the world in slightly different ways. When you write about your experiences, you want your individual view of the world to appear—that's your voice! It's much easier for your voice to come through when you write about the things you know and care about.

Setting Your Voice Free

This lesson is all about putting your voice into your writing. To start, read the list of suggested topics on page 55. You may choose any one of these or use an idea of your own. If you choose a topic that you know and care about, your voice will really come through. Your job is to write a short paragraph, six or seven sentences, and set your voice free.

name: ______ date: ______

- My favorite activity (hiking, soccer, gardening, and so on)
- The last time I said, "I'll never do that again!" (What happened?)
- A person who pesters me
- Helping out at home
- It happened on the playground
- Another idea ______

A Little Help

A little warm-up never hurts. Use one of your prewriting skills to get focused: idea web, word collection, list of questions, a picture, or anything else that helps.

Use this space for your prewriting.

Writing

Remember when you practiced adding voice to flat writing? You tried to bring an idea to life by adding important details and feelings, so that the reader could be part of the experience. Use your prewriting ideas to begin. Remember to set your voice free!

Pause and Reflect

When you have finished writing, read your paragraph aloud quietly. Listen to your words. How would you describe your voice?

My topic or title is

I would describe my voice as

name: .... date: ....

Rating Your Voice

Now that you have tried describing the *kind* of voice you used in your writing, try thinking about your voice in a different way. Use the scale to rate the **strength** and **energy** of your voice. Remember the passage from *The Sign of the Beaver* in Lesson 11? The author uses a quiet but powerfully energized voice to tell about Matt's house and his feelings when his father is quiet. How strong is your voice? How much energy do you have? Rate it here.

1	2	3	4	5	6
Small voice, not much energy.					Big voice, energetic and powerful.

A Writer's Question

What did you discover about your voice today? What is one thing you know you must do to keep your voice strong?

Unit 4

Word Choice

Have you seen how people sometimes get chosen for a baseball or football team? They might try out or line up, and then the coach makes the choices. Well, imagine a big line of words, all waiting to get on your writing team. They're all screaming for your attention, but you're the one who gets to choose which ones you want. Your *word choice* can make the difference between flat, boring writing and lively, interesting writing. How will you know which words can make your writing as strong as it can be?

In this unit, you'll find a few writers' tricks that should help you with word choice. You'll learn about

- choosing verbs that give your writing energy
- learning new words to enliven your writing
- describing with sensory words
- cutting out unnecessary words

Lesson 13

name: .... date: ....

Verbs of Steel

Writers work hard at what they do. They don't just hold out blank sheets of paper, hoping that the right words will fall from the sky and land in the right spots. Good writers are always on the lookout for the exact word to describe a certain shade of red, the way a dog barks at a stranger, or the way a mother lion moves while hunting. Choosing the right *verb,* or action word, is especially important. Strong verbs energize writing. This energy brings out the writer's unique voice.

Sharing an Example: The BFG

In the Roald Dahl classic, *The BFG,* young Sophie sees a giant outside her window in the middle of the night. Because she has seen him, the BFG (**B**ig **F**riendly **G**iant) takes her away to Giant Country. He is kind to her, and together they find a way to stop the other giants and their less-than-friendly ways. Notice that the strong verbs, the "verbs of steel," are in bold print.

Sophie, crouching underneath the blanket, felt strong fingers grasping hold of her, and then she was lifted up from her bed, blanket and all, and whisked out of the window.

If you can think of anything more terrifying than that happening to you in the middle of the night, then let's hear about it.

The awful thing was that Sophie knew exactly what was going on although she couldn't see it happening. She knew that a Monster (or Giant) with an enormous long pale wrinkly face and dangerous eyes had plucked her from her bed in the middle of the witching hour and was now carrying her out through the window smothered in a blanket.

What actually happened next was this. When the Giant had got Sophie outside, he arranged the blanket so that he could grasp all the four corners of it at once in one of his huge hands, with Sophie imprisoned inside. In the other hand he seized the suitcase and the long trumpet thing and off he ran.

Roald Dahl, *The BFG* (New York: Viking Penguin, 1987), p. 17

Goodbye, Strong Verbs

Could you see what was happening to Sophie? How well would the writing work if the author had used weaker verbs? In this version, the strong verbs have been replaced with weaker choices.

Sophie, sitting underneath the blanket, felt strong fingers taking hold of her, and then she was picked up from her bed, blanket and all, and carried out of the window.

If you can think of anything more terrifying than that happening to you in the middle of the night, then let's hear about it.

The awful thing was that Sophie knew exactly what was going on although she couldn't see it happening. She knew that a Monster (or Giant) with an enormous long pale wrinkly face and dangerous eyes had taken her from her bed in the middle of the witching hour and was now carrying her out through the window wrapped in a blanket.

What actually happened next was this. When the Giant had got Sophie outside, he moved the blanket so that he could hold all the four corners of it at once in one of his huge hands, with Sophie held inside. In the other hand he took the suitcase and the long trumpet thing and off he ran.

name: .... date: ....

Your Response

What did you think about the second version? Did you like it, or was the picture it created a little fuzzy?

____ I hardly noticed the difference.

____ It was better.

____ It was dull.

If you thought the second version was a bit dull, you're right. Using plucked in place of taken helps you feel Sophie's fear and surprise. Verbs like whisked, imprisoned, seized, and smothered really show the BFG's speed and determination. You can almost feel things happening. Remember, verbs add power to your ideas and to your voice.

Finding Verbs of Steel

Read the next passage from a student writer. Underline any verbs that are strong and powerful enough to be "verbs of steel."

The Lemonade Stand

It wasn't really so much of a stand as it was an old wooden box flipped on its side. No matter what we did, it slanted a bit to the left and creaked every time we set the pitcher of lemonade down. My sister and I prayed it would hold together for at least today.

After scraping and scrounging every bit of change we could find, we needed only five dollars more to get the scooter we had been dreaming of for weeks. Today was supposed to be warm, and everyone in the neighborhood would be outside clipping branches, yanking weeds, and mowing lawns. It would be a perfect day for gulping down glass after glass of cool lemonade. We were going to haul in a fortune today.

name: ______________________ date: ____________

Share and Compare

With a partner, share your underlined verbs. Did both of you underline the same "verbs of steel"? Why did you make the choices you did?

Your Own Steel

Now it's time to practice putting powerful verbs into your own writing. Choose a topic from the list or use an idea of your own. Write a paragraph with at least six sentences. Focus on choosing strong verbs that will bring your idea to life. Underline the verbs you think are especially powerful. Remember that this practice is all about choosing the right words to match the idea in your head. If you don't like what you write the first time, choose another way to say it.

- An experience you had trying to earn money
- Something you've been saving your money for
- Playing on a warm, sunny day
- A family outing
- Your own idea ______________________

____

____

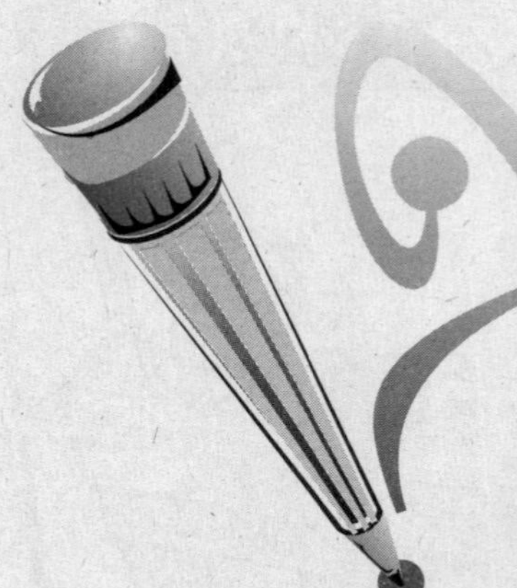

A Writer's Question

What would you say to a writer who asked, "What's the big deal with strong verbs?" How would you persuade the writer that verbs are important?

name: .... date: ....

Using Context

Choosing every word that goes into your writing gives you freedom and power as a writer. However, choosing is more fun when you know lots of words to choose from. Reading is probably the best way to bump into new words that can expand your vocabulary. We hope you are already an *avid* reader who reads anything and everything you can get your hands on.

Hey, there's a word that might be new to you—*avid.* Do you know what it means? What if you don't? You can look at the context, or the way the word is used in a sentence or paragraph. Can you guess what *avid* means by looking at the rest of the sentence? If you said "interested or enthusiastic," you would be right! Now, you can add *avid* to your bank of words to choose from the next time you write.

name: .... date: ....

Words out of Context

Context Clues

To show you how important context is, look at this list of lonesome words. They are all on their own without the help of sentences. It's much harder to figure out what each word means without the aid of a sentence, but give it a try. Read the list on your own, and then read it again with a partner. Together, think about what each word *might* mean. If you don't know, make a guess, and write what you think in the column called Possible Meanings. Don't forget that words can have more than one meaning, so let your brain come up with all kinds of ideas.

	Possible Meanings	Meaning from Context
1. contented		
2. wallowing		
3. delectable		
4. succulent		
5. pathetic		
6. aristocrat		
7. descendant		
8. ancestors		
9. resisted		
10. sentimental		
11. blissful		
12. abrupt		

name: .... date: ....

Putting Words Back in Context

In this part of the lesson, we are going to put the words back into the sentences they came from—back in context, that is. These words all come from the book, *I, Crocodile,* about a crocodile taken from Egypt to Paris by the Emperor Napoleon of France. The words from the list are in purple print so that you can spot them easily. As you read the passage, see whether you can use the context of each sentence to help you figure out the meaning of each word. You can still make a guess, but this time you've got the context to help you! With your partner, write what you *think* the meaning of each word might be in the right-hand column. It's possible that the ideas in this column will be very different from what you wrote in the left-hand column.

I, Crocodile

Ah, what a contented crocodile I used to be. Wallowing around in slimy green water. . . Snoozing on mudbanks in the hot sun . . . Scaring the life out of anything that wandered by.

But my greatest joy? Eating! (Actually, overeating.)

I had the perfect diet. An endless variety of delectable fish, all sorts of succulent water birds, plus a few reptiles on the side—distant cousins only.

However, unlike certain pathetic creatures who have to chase after their next meal, I always ate in style. Dinner? It came to me!

And why not? I'm an aristocrat. A direct descendant of the noble crocodiles of ancient Egypt. In fact, the great Pharaohs themselves treated my ancestors like gods!

Idol worship—I just love it! That's why I always resisted eating people, even though they do look awfully tasty. Guess I'm just the sentimental type.

Those were the blissful days, indeed. But sadly they came to an abrupt end on (to be precise) August 17, 1799.

Fred Marcellino, *I, Crocodile* (New York: Harper Collins, 1999)

name: .... date: ....

Discuss and Check

With the class, discuss what you think each word means. Talk about the specific context clues you used to help guide your guesses. After you talk about the word meanings, use a dictionary to check the definitions.

A Writer's Question

If you are always ready to find new words to add to your writer's vocabulary, your writing will never be dull. An *avid* writer needs lots of words to choose from. There were twelve words on the list in this lesson. How many were new to you? Choose one of these new words, and try it out in a sentence. Write a sentence that makes the meaning clear from context. Then share your sentence with a partner to see whether you succeeded!

Lesson 15

name: .... date: ....

Painting Word Pictures

Choosing the right words helps "paint pictures" in your reader's mind. If you want those pictures to be vivid—so vivid your reader feels right there at the scene with you—you need words that connect to the senses of sight, hearing, touch, smell, and taste. These words are called *sensory* words. Using them pulls your readers right into your writing.

Sharing an Example: Mud Fights

Here is an example of sensory language used by a student author. It is easy to tell that Jocelyn really enjoyed these "Mud Fights" with her friend. Find the **sensory** words that paint a picture in your mind.

Seeing
Touching
Hearing
Tasting
Smelling

Mud Fights

by Jocelyn Noonan

When we had nothing better to do,
Katie and I
Would get out our dads' oldest t-shirts
And take off our shoes.
Then we would go out to the edge of the property
Where there was a soft circle of dust.
Katie would turn on the hose
And I would spray.

name: .... date: ....

Then we would squish the earth
Between our toes
Until it was cool and wet.
It always started out
With tiny mud droplets,
But soon we would be
Heaving giant handfuls of it,
Tripping, stumbling, screaming,
But giggling happily the whole time.
And eventually we would find ourselves
Stuck in the ooze,
And we would collapse
Into it and on top of each other,
And lie there laughing
Until muddy tears streamed out of our eyes.

Sensory Reaction

Did Jocelyn use many sensory details in her poem? With a partner, look at the poem again. With your pencil, underline any sensory details you notice. Then compare notes with your partner. See whether you noticed the same things.

Do you feel as though you're right in the middle of the muddy battle? Why? Well, Jocelyn has chosen sensory details to help readers feel the ooze and mud and lie there laughing with her! If we grouped all her **sensory details** into a chart, it might look like this:

I see	I hear	I touch	I smell	I taste
old t-shirts	screaming	earth between toes, cool, wet		mud droplets
circle of dust	giggling		cool, wet earth	muddy tears
tiny droplets		tripping, stumbling		
giant handfuls	laughing	stuck in the ooze		

name: .... date: ....

Look carefully at the chart on page 68 with your partner, and then look at the language you underlined in Jocelyn's poem. Do you see some of the same words and phrases? Probably you do, and that means you were able to spot sensory details in writing. Maybe you even found some things we missed!

Making Your Own Chart

Here's a piece of Gabe's descriptive writing about cleaning the garage. Read it, looking and listening for sensations of sight, sound, smell, taste, or touch. (You might not find them all!) First, underline any part that you think is an example of sensory language. Then list each detail on the chart that follows.

Cleaning the Garage

The "Big Saturday Clean-up" was all about living up to the promise my parents made when they bought our house. They had promised to keep the garage clean enough so the car would fit, but all those dusty boxes stuffed with stale-smelling junk meant the car stayed outside. So there I was on the hottest Saturday in June, in my grubby work pants with the grass stains and my paint-flecked T-shirt, standing on the hot blacktop driveway wondering where to start. Was I out there sweating and getting a sunburn because I'm the world's greatest kid? Was I going to dig through musty boxes smelling of grease and old grungy rags out of the goodness of my heart? No. Mom had offered me a crisp twenty-dollar bill, iced tea whenever I asked, and frosty root beer popsicles every hour. (I could almost feel the cool ice melting on my tongue.) To top it off, I could play rock music on my boom box as loud as I wanted. She knew how to get me to say yes.

I see	I hear	I touch	I smell	I taste

name: date:

Your Turn to Write!

Picture yourself faced with a chore you'd rather not do or in the middle of a really fun time with a friend. Make some notes here as a way of prewriting.

I see ______

I hear ______

I taste ______

I touch ______

I smell ______

Now, use your sensory detail notes to write either a short poem or a paragraph at least six sentences long.

______

______

______

______

______

Share

When you have finished writing, read your poem or paragraph aloud to hear how it sounds. Did you include all the important sensory details to paint a complete picture of your idea?

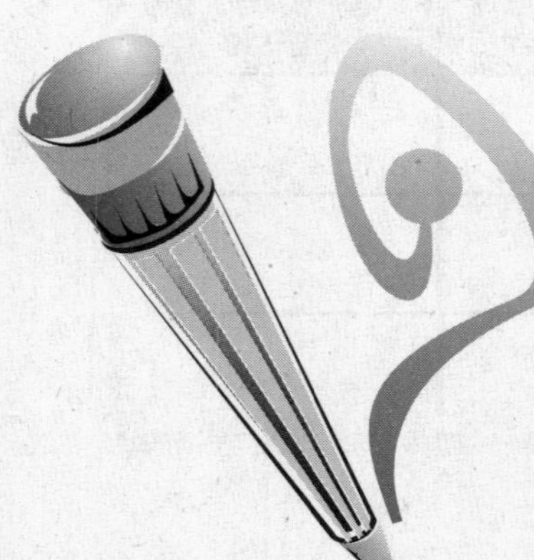

A Writer's Question

Of the five senses—sight, hearing, taste, touch, and smell—which is the easiest for you to include in the sensory details in your own writing? Why?

name: .... date: ....

Pop That Balloon—Revise to Clarify

What happens when you blow air into a balloon? Well, eventually the balloon is so full that you can't get another breath into it, and its sides feel tight and ready to pop! You have to let some air out. The same kind of thing happens when a writer gets carried away with words. Sometimes a writer uses too many words, and the writing begins to swell up like a balloon "It was a gray, dark, rainy, wet, cloudy, stormy, carry-your-umbrella sort of day." You couldn't cram another word into that sentence—you'd better take some words out! Good writers know that it's important to choose a *few* strong words and leave out unnecessary words.

Sharing an Example: A Forest Full of Trees, Animals, Other Living Creatures, and a Trail

This writer is eager to tell us *everything* about hiking through the woods. Does she overdo details and descriptive words? Is this a "big balloon" paragraph? Could you let some air out? In other words, could you take out any words without changing the main idea?

name: .... date: ....

It was actually rather late on a beautiful and wonderful Sunday afternoon, right around 4 o'clock. Quick as a flash, a magnificent idea suddenly popped into my dad's cranium. "Let's go for an adventure hike in the Nature Park," he retorted happily, while smiling joyfully. He adored the Nature Park. The Nature Park is a gorgeous beautifully forested area with a trail winding back and forth through it like a snake winding back and forth through the green grass. The winding trail is marked with small, little nature signs with informational data and facts about the amazing plant life, animal life, insects, and trees that can be discovered as you hike along the winding path that's like a trail. It is honestly and truly an absolutely amazing slice of nature. I agreed that a walk through the Nature Park would be the perfect way to top off a grand and glorious Sunday afternoon.

Your Response

How did this writing look and sound to you?

____ A little overwritten, but not that bad

____ Just about right

____ Way too wordy and overwritten—a huge balloon paragraph.

____ needs more descriptive words

Now read the passage again with a partner. Cross out any unnecessary words or sentences. Circle any words or sentences that need to be changed, and show how you would change them. Keep the main idea clear and strong, but make every word count.

Checking Out Our Revision: The Nature Park

Read the revised passage on page 73. Compare the revisions to what you and your partner circled or crossed out. Did you make the same corrections?

name: .... date: ....

It was around 4 o'clock on Sunday afternoon. Suddenly, a great idea popped into my dad's head. "Let's go for a hike in the Nature Park!" he said with a smile. He really loves that park. The Nature Park is a beautiful forested area with a trail that winds through it like a snake. Along the trail, there are little signs filled with information about interesting plants, birds, and animals that you might find along the way. It is a totally cool place, so of course I said, "Let's go!"

Share and Compare

How does this revision compare with what you did? Which one of these is true for you and your partner?

____ We cut out and changed even more than you did!

____ We cut out and changed about the same amount that you did.

____ We did not cut out or change as much, but we like the results.

____ We did not cut out or change as much, and next time we would make more changes.

Revising to Clarify: The "Big" City

Here is another overwritten passage that needs your help. Read the passage carefully. Cross out unnecessary words, and circle any parts that should be changed. Then rewrite the passage on a separate piece of paper. Remember that you want each word to be right for that sentence and for the main idea. (**Hint:** You can change the punctuation as you make changes in the sentences if you need to. For example, you might want to add or move a period.)

My family, all of us, my mom, dad, and two sisters come from a very small, little town. This tiny, minute village where we reside is so miniature that there are only two stores, a gas station, and a post office. There is almost nothing, zero, zip, nada, for active, rowdy, fun-loving kids like us to do when we are not spending time gaining educational skills. Our place of education, also known as our school, is really more like something from *Little House on the Prairie,* with all grades required to be in one teeny tiny small location, making for very cramped conditions. Of all the many important things I have managed to learn in my many days of school, the most significant, important thing is that this town is far too limited in its opportunities. When we can, as soon as we're able, I want my family to move out, and leave this place of residence far behind.

Share and Compare

Share your revised paragraph with your partner. Look closely at the kinds of changes each of you made. Was one version shorter? Did you think one version was a little stronger and clearer than the other? Talk about how you decided what to cut and what to change.

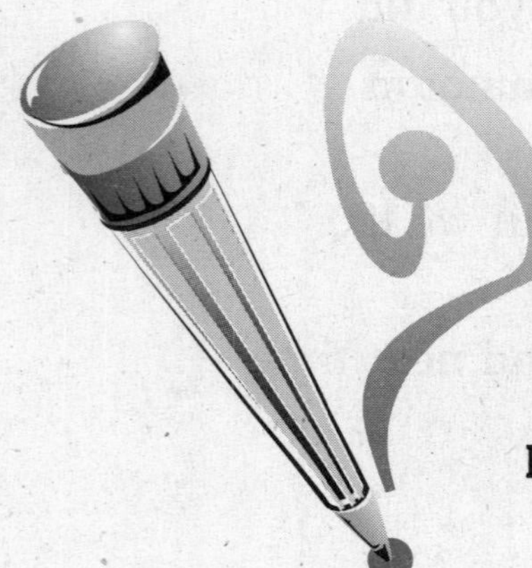

A Writer's Question

How good were you at finding things to revise in this overwritten passage? Rate yourself from 1 to 6, with 1 being the lowest and 6 being the highest.

1	2	3	4	5	6
I need more practice!					I cut every word that wasn't needed.

Unit 5

Sentence Fluency

By now you know that good writing has clear, well-organized ideas. It rings with voice, and the words are well chosen. All these traits help make writing stronger. In this unit you'll learn about another quality that's equally important: sentence fluency.

A good way to test sentence fluency is to read a passage aloud. If the passage is fluent, the reading comes easily. The writing has rhythm, a kind of natural flow that's easy on the ear. One sentence just seems to glide right into the next. This makes reading easy and fun, too.

In this unit, you'll work on making your sentences more fluent and natural. You'll learn about

- varying your sentence beginnings
- rewriting run-on sentences
- making language sound natural
- checking for smoothness and flow

Lesson 17

name: .... date: ....

Spice Up Your Sentences

Imagine a book in which every sentence begins the same way: "The dog was old. The dog was black. The dog had been sleeping. The dog felt hungry now. The dog started to eat." Does your brain feel numb yet? "Variety is the spice of life" is an old saying that applies well to writing. Good writing keeps the reader interested and eager to read more. Variety in your sentence beginnings spices up your writing and helps the reader stay alert—just the way you want a reader to be.

Sharing an Example: The Cricket in Times Square

In the classic story *The Cricket in Times Square,* author George Selden shows the importance of varying sentence beginnings. In this passage, Mario, a boy whose parents own a newsstand in Times Square, hears a sound he hasn't heard before in the busy station. It turns out to be Chester the cricket. Read the passage. Notice the sentence beginnings. The first few words of each sentence are highlighted to help you compare them.

name: .... date: ....

Mario heard the sound too. He stood up and listened intently. The noise of the shuttle rattled off into silence. From the streets above came the quiet murmur of the late traffic. There was a noise of rustling nothingness in the station. Still Mario listened, straining to catch the mysterious sound . . . And there it came again.

It was like a quick stroke across the strings of a violin, or like a harp that had been plucked suddenly. If a leaf in a green forest far from New York had fallen at midnight through the darkness into a thicket, it might have sounded like that.

Mario thought he knew what it was. The summer before he had gone to visit a friend who lived on Long Island. One afternoon, as the low sun reached long yellow fingers through the tall grass, he had stopped beside a meadow to listen to just such a noise. But there had been many of them then—a chorus. Now there was only one. Faintly it came again through the subway station.

George Selden, *The Cricket in Times Square* (New York: Yearling, 1960), p. 9

Your Response

How much variety in sentence beginnings did you see and hear?

____ a lot of variety ____ a little variety ____ no variety

Did you like the sound and the flow of this passage? What if George Selden had written it with little or no variety, like this: "Mario thought he knew what it was. Mario had gone to visit a friend who lived on Long Island. Mario had stopped beside a meadow. Mario had listened to just such a noise." Would the writing be as interesting? Would it have the same smooth flow? Why?

Writer's Tip: When you are writing, you don't have to begin every sentence in a new way. If you want to keep your readers interested, however, it's important to use a variety of beginnings.

name: .... date: ....

Revising "Block Party"

This next writing sample has a fluency problem. To uncover the problem, underline the first three words of each sentence.

Block Party

We had a block party on July 4 to celebrate the holiday and get to know our neighbors. We called the police and asked whether it would be all right to close off each end of our street so that we could have a party. We put up orange traffic cones with a sign that told everyone what we were doing. We decided who would bring their barbecues out to the street, and one person took charge of buying hamburgers and hot dogs. We thought each family could bring their own beverages, so there wouldn't be any complaining. We could tell that everyone seemed to have a real good time, especially the younger kids who had never been in the street.

Time to Spice It Up

What did you notice about this passage? Was it a pleasure to read? If you're thinking that it's time to revise and add variety, you're right. Change or add words, and remember that you may need to change the punctuation. Write your revision in the space below.

Independence Day

name: .... date: ....

____

____

____

____

____

____

____

____

Share and Compare

Read your whole paragraph aloud to a partner. Reading aloud is the best way to hear the fluency in a piece of writing. Compare what you wrote to the first version. How does it sound? Let your partner help you rate it.

____ So much better! I used a lot of variety to spice up the sentences.

____ It's about the same. I still need more variety.

____ It sounds exactly the same. All my sentences still begin the same way.

A Writer's Question

What is the best way to end this sentence (other than "the spice of life") and turn it into a new and catchy saying that will help other writers? Be ready to share your sentence with the class.

Variety is ____

____.

Lesson 18

name: .... date: ....

Just Say No to Run-ons

Drivers need signs that tell them where to stop. Otherwise, they might run right through intersections. This kind of driving leads to tickets—or crashes! Readers, too, look for signs. For example, periods tell them where to stop. If the writer forgets to use signs, readers may plow headlong into one or more *run-on sentences.* Readers don't get tickets for this. They get confused, however, and they run out of breath.

Most run-ons are really two or more complete sentences hooked together to make one big sentence. This kind of run-on is easy to fix. You put a period at the end of one sentence, and insert a capital letter at the start of the next one. Other run-ons stretch out longer. They are many short thoughts hooked together by connecting words: *and, and so, then, and then, because, so then,* and so on. This kind of run-on takes a little more fixing, but don't worry—it's time well spent. Your readers won't be getting headaches from collisions with run-ons.

name: .... date: ....

Sharing an Example: Stone Fox

Here's a short passage from John Reynolds Gardiner's book, *Stone Fox.* You are going to see three versions of this passage. The first and second versions have been changed to demonstrate run-on problems. The third version is exactly the way the author wrote it. Notice how the run-ons affect the flow of the writing.

Run-on Problem 1: Missing Periods and Capital Letters

In the next week little Willy and Searchlight went over the ten-mile track every day, until they knew every inch of it by heart Stone Fox hardly practiced at all in fact, little Willy only saw Stone Fox do the course once, and then he wasn't going very fast the race was scheduled for Saturday at ten o'clock.

Zoom In!

This passage looks like one long sentence. What do *you* think? Do you hear more than one sentence? Put a period in each place you think a sentence ends, and add capital letters where they are needed. Then compare your work with your partner's work. Did both of you hear sentences end in the same spots?

Run-on Problem 2: Too Many Connecting Words

In the next week little Willy and Searchlight went over the ten-mile track every day, until they knew every inch of it by heart **but** Stone Fox hardly practiced at all **and** in fact, little Willy only saw Stone Fox do the course once, **and then** he wasn't going very fast **so** the race was scheduled for Saturday at ten o'clock.

name: .... date: ....

Zoom In!

This "sentence" takes a big breath to read aloud, don't you think? (Try it!) Try putting a period in place of the extra connecting words (**boldfaced** words). Then, read the result aloud to a partner. How does it sound now?

The Author's Version: No Run-ons!

In the next week little Willy and Searchlight went over the ten-mile track every day, until they knew every inch of it by heart.

Stone Fox hardly practiced at all. **I**n fact, little Willy only saw Stone Fox do the course once, and then he wasn't going very fast.

The race was scheduled for Saturday at ten o'clock.

John Reynolds Gardiner, *Stone Fox* (New York: Harper and Row, 1980), pp. 53–54

Zoom In!

The author actually wrote this as four separate sentences in three separate paragraphs. Did you guess that? (____ Yes, I also thought it was four sentences. ____ No, I thought it was a different number.) This version is clear, easy to read, and has the rhythm or fluency the author wants for this story.

Some Practice

Here are two different pieces of writing for you to work on. Zoom in on each piece of writing, and ask whether you should add periods and capitals or take out connecting words before adding periods and capitals. Write your revisions on the text.

Sample 1

The big dog was chasing him down the street and it seemed that the dog was running almost as fast as he could pedal his bike so he tried to lose the dog by turning sharply down an alley but the dog stayed right with him and he was running out of ideas and energy.

name: .... date: ....

Sample 2

I could hear the sound from across the street and it was a loud, whining, chain saw sort of sound and it was coming from the neighbor's backyard so then suddenly the sound stopped but then there was a sharp crack and so a tree behind their house began to fall but I couldn't see it hit the ground but then I heard it.

Share and Compare

When you have finished revising the two run-on sentences, share your new sentences with a partner. Be sure to read both sets of revisions aloud. Do they sound alike? Do both revisions work? Did both you and your partner say "no" to run-ons?

A Writer's Question

What happens to the rhythm or fluency of writing when sentences run on and on? Share your thoughts here.

____

____

____

____

Lesson 19

name: .... date: ....

Authentic Conversation

Whether it's two kids talking about video games in a modern story or two young soldiers talking about a battle in a Civil War story, what characters say to one another should sound real. The conversation between characters in stories is called *dialogue.* Dialogue helps readers get inside characters' minds and understand the characters better. But this only works when dialogue sounds smooth and flows naturally, like a real conversation.

Sharing an Example: No Man's Land

A conversation between a soldier and a commanding officer has its own sense of rhythm and sounds very different from the way two friends would discuss the day's events. Here is a bit of dialogue between a young Confederate soldier and an officer who asks him to explain his recent actions. As you read, ask yourself, "Do these people sound like real soldiers talking?"

name: .... date: ....

Major Wilmot was rubbing his shoulder as he listened to Hazen's excuses. . . .

"Did you call out?" asked the Major.
"Yes, sir," said Hazen.
"Order them to show themselves?"
"Yes, sir."
"Ask for the password?"
"Yes, sir."
"When they didn't comply, you fired?"
"They didn't give the password, sir."

A group of men guffawed. Wilmot silenced them with a stern look. "Then you are to be commended for following orders," said Wilmot. "No harm done, aside from rousing your fellow soldiers from their sleep."

Susan Bartoletti, *No Man's Land* (New York: Scholastic, 1999), pp. 28–29

Your Response

You haven't been a soldier, but you are a young person who has had to talk with adults in charge: parents, teachers, coaches, and so on. Did this dialogue sound like a major in the army talking to someone in his command?

____ Yes, it sounded just the way real people would talk in this kind of situation.

____ No, it did not sound anything like real soldiers talking.

____ I am not sure. I couldn't really tell.

Authentic Dialogue

Let's look at another example. This time, you can make changes in the dialogue if you like. If you make changes, remember that you are trying to make the dialogue sound authentic—the way real people would talk in the same situation.

In the example on page 86, Detective Schneider is questioning Ian, a fourth grader who witnessed the theft of a bike.

name: .... date: ....

Detective Schneider and Ian stood next to the bike rack in front of the school. This was the third school that had reported stolen bikes. The detective wanted to get to the bottom of this before it happened again.

"So, dude, like, did you see someone messing with the bikes?" Detective Schneider asked, looking up in the air.

"Why, yes, detective," Ian replied, trying to look the detective in the eyes. "I did happen to observe a shady looking character lingering by the bike rack at approximately 7:55 this morning."

"Whoa! Dude, you're not dissing me are you? I mean, like, how do you know the exact time?" Detective Schneider looked a bit confused.

"Why, sir, I was wearing a watch, and all it took was a brief glance. Besides, sir," Ian said with a smile, "I have carefully kept track of the arrival time of that bus for several months as part of a project."

"Whoa!" was all that came out of the detective's mouth.

Do Ian and Detective Schneider sound like real people talking?

____ Yes, real fourth graders and detectives sound just like them.

____ No, they don't sound like a real student and police officer to me.

Maybe this writer needs your help to make this conversation sound more authentic. Work with a partner to revise the dialogue between Ian and Detective Schneider. You may change any words. It should still be about witnessing the theft of a bike, though.

A Suggestion: Here's a plan to help you make the conversation sound more real. You choose one character (Detective Schneider or Ian) and have your partner take the

name: .... date: ....

other character. One of you will start the dialogue by writing one line; then the other will write what he or she would say in real life, and so on. Continue until each of you has written three lines, six lines altogether. Let the dialogue flow, and keep it authentic!

____

____

____

____

____

____

Share

After you have finished writing, read your dialogue aloud. Does the dialogue sound as natural and smooth as when you wrote it? If not, change the language to make it stronger.

A Writer's Question

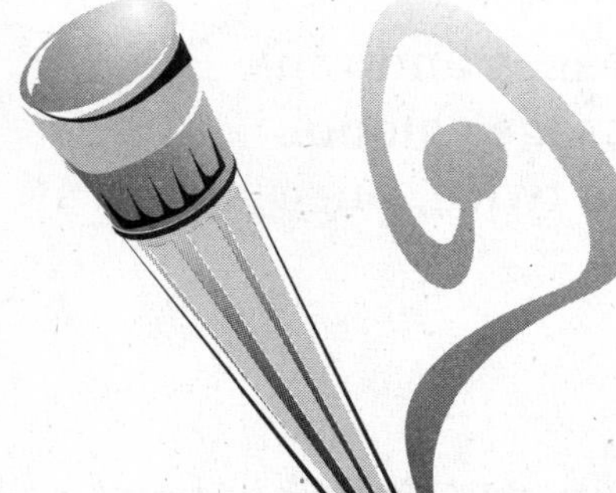

If you are going to put dialogue in your writing, pay attention to the way people talk to one another in daily life. Think back to a conversation you had recently with someone in authority. What were you talking about? Did one of you do more talking than the other? How would you describe the way this person talked? How would you describe the way you talked?

Conversation topic: ______________________________

Who was involved? ______________________________

I would describe the way I talked as ______________________________

I would describe the way the other person talked as ______________________________

____

name: .... date: ....

Read and Rank

Smooth, fluent writing begs to be read aloud. When writing is fluent, it's truly a pleasure to hear and feel the rhythm of the words and sentences as they roll off your tongue. In fact, reading a piece of writing aloud is probably the best way to find out how fluent that writing is. So remember, whenever you're checking fluency, use your voice and your ears.

Putting Them in Order: Read and Rank

With a partner, read the following three passages and rank them for fluency. Take turns reading the passages aloud. This gives you a chance to hear each passage twice, once as a reader and once as a listener.

Sample A

I am always so nervous whenever I have to get up and speak in front of my class. My knees get shaky. Never make eye contact with friends. That will throw you way off. Instead of looking right into their eyes, pick a spot just over the top of their heads. This will make it seem like you're looking at them when you're actually not. Your throat can get dry and you might cough and need water, but if there isn't any, you're stuck, which can be embarrassing and ruin your presentation grade, which could get you in trouble.

name: .... date: ....

Sample B

I've always been told that if you have to give a speech or do a presentation for your class, volunteer to go first. Now, this may seem like tough advice, especially if you are the kind who gets nervous in front of people. But here's the cool part. If you go first, you're done! You can sit back, relax, and watch everyone else wait nervously for his or her turn. Besides, when you're first, there isn't anyone to be compared to. No one can say your speech wasn't as good as so-and-so's, and after a couple of speeches, people aren't even thinking about you anymore. The pressure is off. Going first is the only way to go.

Sample C

Sweaty palms. Shaky knees. I get these when I have to speak in front of my class. It's bad. I don't like it. I get other kinds of things, too. Dry throat. And what if you're not really ready but it's your turn to go and you have to go or your grade goes down and if your grade goes down then you can get grounded, which is not very fun. Blurry vision. I get that, too, and it's not good. It doesn't help. I don't like it because I get so nervous. I've dropped note cards on the floor before. That is not good. I don't like it. Perspiration can be a problem on your forehead and arms and top lip.

Voice Rankings

Rank the three pieces for fluency by putting letter **A, B,** or **C** in the blank where it fits.

____ Smooth and fluent. A pleasure to read aloud.

____ So-so on the fluency. Some smooth parts, some rough spots.

____ A struggle to read with any rhythm. Choppy and awkward.

name: ______________________ date: ____________

Sharing an Example: Komodo Dragons

Here are two versions of a passage from the book, *Creepy Creatures,* by Sneed B. Collard III. The first version has been changed to create some fluency problems. The second version is just the way the author wrote it.

Komodo dragons are the biggest lizards in the world. They are also called "oras." They can be ten feet long from end to end. They can live as long as fifty years. You can't tell their age. They are big so they can catch all kinds of things to eat. Oras use their tongues to smell food. They have an excellent sense of smell. They usually run away when they smell a human. They live on six islands in Indonesia.

Zoom In!

Does this paragraph flow like a river, or does it seem more like an elevator stopping on every floor? If this piece isn't smooth and fluent, what is the problem?

____ There is no fluency problem. It's as smooth as melting ice cream.

____ There IS a fluency problem, and it's this: ______________

____

How can you make this piece more fluent? Remember to read aloud as you work. It will help you smooth out the bumps that break the flow.

____

____

____

____

____

____

____

____

name: .... date: ....

Following is the author's original. Think about fluency as you read it.

"Komodo Dragons" (the author's version)

Komodo dragons or "oras" are the world's largest lizards. Oras grow to ten feet long from snout to tail. Experts believe oras live as long as fifty years, but no one is sure. There's no good way to tell an ora's age, and these lizards never have birthday parties. An ora's enormous size lets it catch and eat everything from grasshoppers to goats. Oras use their tongues to smell food, and their sense of smell is excellent. Don't worry though, oras usually run away when they smell a human being—and they will smell you only if you go to one of the six tiny islands in Indonesia where they live.

Sneed B. Collard III, "Komodo Dragons" in *Creepy Creatures* (Watertown, MA: Charlesbridge, 1992)

Zoom In!

Compare the writer's version with your revision. Which one is more fluent?

____ His original is more fluent.

____ I think mine is just about as fluent!

____ Mine is even MORE fluent!

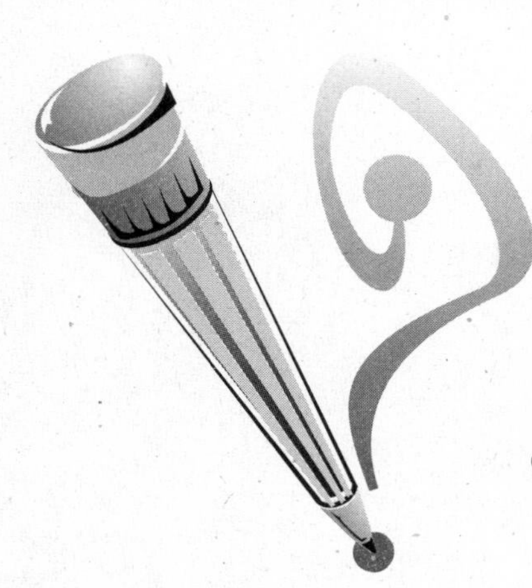

A Writer's Question

What advice would you give a writer who isn't sure how to rate the fluency in his or her writing?

Unit 6

Conventions

As you may know, editing calls for noticing, marking, and then fixing mistakes. The mistakes might be in spelling, punctuation, grammar, paragraphing, or any number of things. These are the *conventions* of writing that you as an editor are in charge of checking.

Editing is usually the last thing you do to a piece of writing. After you have revised your work for ideas, organization, voice, word choice, and sentence fluency, you take one more look to make sure you have no errors to trip up your reader.

This unit will give you some tips for becoming a good editor. You'll learn about

- revising and editing
- using an editor's marks
- seeing and hearing errors
- making your own editing checklist

name: .... date: ....

What's the Difference?

Would you say that basketball and football are the same because both involve using a ball to score points? No—no more than making a cake and roasting a turkey are the same because both involve using an oven to get results. Let's try another question: Would you say that *revising* and *editing* are the same because both involve using special techniques to improve your writing? Right you are—the answer is no! These two skills are different. In the lesson, you'll learn how to tell them apart and how to use them to make your sentences score big and your paragraphs really cook!

What's on Your Mind? First Thoughts . . .

Let's start with asking two important questions: What is **revising?** What is **editing?** Write whatever comes to mind.

Revising is ______________________________________

____.

Editing is ______________________________________

____.

name: .... date: ....

Revising and Editing in Action

Look carefully at the **Before** and **After** examples that follow. In each case, the writer has made some changes. What kinds of changes are they?

Sentences with errors — Revising and Editing Machine — Sentences without errors

Revising calls for BIG changes—like these:

Before: To wash your car, first get it very wet by spraying it with a hose. Don't take time to eat lunch. Next, get a bucket, car soap, and a scrubber mitt.

After: To wash your car, first make sure it is parked in the driveway or on the street. Get a bucket, car soap, and a scrubber mitt. Then, wet the car down with a hose.

What happened? Look closely at the two versions, **Before** and **After.** What is different? List some changes the writer made.

____

____

____

Editing calls for smaller changes—like these:

Before: To wash your, frist make sure it is parked in the driveway or on the street. before wetting it down with a hose, get a bucket, car soap, and a scrubber mitt.

After: To wash your car, first make sure it is parked in the driveway or on the street. Before wetting it down with a hose, get a bucket, car soap, and a scrubber mitt.

What happened? Look closely at the two versions, **Before** and **After.** What is different? List some changes the writer made.

____

____

____

name: .... date: ....

Revising or Editing: Narrowing It Down

Are these two terms becoming clear in your mind? Read each of the following examples carefully. Decide whether each item is an example of **revising** or **editing.** Then mark your choice with an **X**.

1. Correcting the spelling of *"Sincearly"* (Sincerely) in the closing of a letter.

____ **Revising** ____ **Editing**

2. Changing the sentence "It was a pretty sunset" to "The sky was on fire with flames of red and yellow as the sun slipped below the horizon."

____ **Revising** ____ **Editing**

3. Rewriting the ending of a story to make it work better.

____ **Revising** ____ **Editing**

4. Indenting to show the beginning of a new paragraph.

____ **Revising** ____ **Editing**

5. Fixing a run-on sentence.

____ **Revising** ____ **Editing**

6. Reorganizing the steps in a recipe for making a cake.

____ **Revising** ____ **Editing**

Share and Compare

Share your responses with a partner. Did you agree on where to put your X's? Discuss any items you did not agree on.

name: .... date: ....

Your Own Definitions

Try again to define *revising* and *editing*. Don't forget that these are action words—things writers do. What you write should show that you understand what each term means. It should also show how revising and editing are different. Ready? Go!

Revising is ______________________________

______________________________.

Editing is ______________________________

______________________________.

Share and Compare

Meet with a partner to share your definitions. It's all right to revise your definitions after you share. You may also want to look back at your first definitions. Did your ideas change much? Were your definitions like your partner's? Does your whole class share the same ideas when it comes to revising and editing?

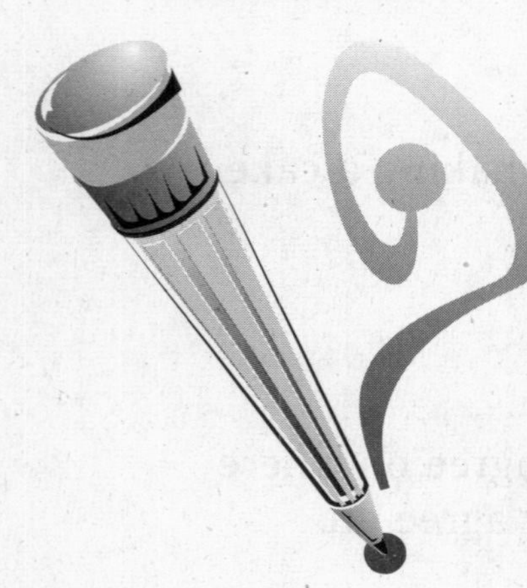

A Writer's Question

Look at your definitions once more, and then think about your writing. Which is easier for you, revising or editing? Explain why.

name: .... date: ....

Reading the Signs

It takes an editor's sharp eye and ear to find mistakes in spelling, punctuation, capitalization, or any other part of a piece of writing. When the editor has done his or her job, it's still up to the writer to correct the errors. At times the writer and the editor are the same person. That person might do both jobs!

An editor "speaks" to a writer with special symbols called editor's marks. These marks identify various errors so that the writer knows what kind of fixing is needed. As a writer, you need to know how to "read" and use these marks. As an editor, you need to know how and when to use these marks in noting errors. If you are both writer and editor, using the editor's marks is like writing little notes to yourself about how to correct your work.

name: .... date: ....

Seven Editor's Marks

In this lesson, you will review five important editor's marks. You will also add two new ones to your editor's toolbox. Don't worry if all seven are new to you. Here's a handy chart with all the marks and their meanings for you to use while you practice. Remember that an editor's mark simply means, "There's a mistake here. Fix it, please." Look carefully at the seven marks to see what they mean and how to use them.

Mark	Meaning	Use
1. ℘	Take it out.	Help is a on the way.
2. ∧	Add a word.	Scooter is my cat.
3. ≡	Capitalize this letter.	My name is andrew.
4. /	Make this a lowercase letter.	She is My dog.
5. ⊙	Add a period.	It is raining⊙
6. ∧,	Add a comma.	I like red, blue, and black.
7. ∨'	Add an apostrophe.	The car is Andrew's toy.

name: .... date: ....

A Little Practice

One important reason for using editor's marks is that it's faster than writing out directions. A writer can interpret the editor's marks and get right to work. Using the marks also keeps the writer responsible for learning how to fix the errors. This way the writer is really involved in every step of the writing process. Here are four practice sentences. Your job is to "read" the editor's marks and write what needs to be done. Look back at the chart if you need to.

1. Nates dog ran out into street.

   What needs to be done? ______________________

   ____

2. some of my favorite foods are pizza green beans and rice.

   What needs to be done? ______________________

   ____

3. The Weather has been ~~and~~ great on our vacation

   What needs to be done? ______________________

   ____

4. Dont step the wet Concrete.

   What needs to be done? ______________________

   ____

Share and Compare

With a partner, share and compare your ideas about what needed to be done in each sentence. Were you able to crack the code and interpret the editor's language?

name: .... date: ....

Put on Your Editor's Hat

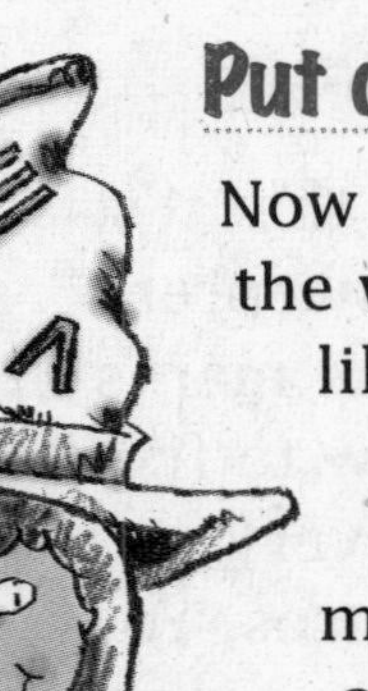

Now you get to be the editor. Use the marks to help the writer of this paragraph. You'll need to "speak" like an editor by using the right marks to tell the writer what needs to be done. (You don't have to *fix* the mistakes you find. Just put in the marks. Pretend that someone else will do the actual fixing.) Look back at the chart if you can't recall the right mark.

Waking Up

I sometimes have the a hard time Waking up. my parents do all kinds of things to get out bed They open my my curtains gently call out my name and my dad will even read to me from a Favorite book. Theyre pretty nice about it I guess Im just not a morning person. Whats so bad about in sleeping in?

Check Your Work

With your partner, check your work. Did you find the same mistakes? Did you use the same marks? How did it feel to be the one putting in the marks?

A Writer's Question

Think about your own writing and the kinds of mistakes you sometimes make. Choose one kind of error you would like to avoid in the future. What is something you can do while you're writing to keep that mistake from happening?

name: .... date: ....

The Eye and the Ear of the Editor

Editing takes more than a sharp pencil. It takes a sharp eye and ear, too. Some mistakes catch your eye easily—they just look wrong. Other errors seem to shout at you—they just sound wrong. To catch these errors, it helps to read the writing aloud. This way your eyes get to see and your ears get to hear. Together they make an error-hunting team that's tough to beat. Don't worry about finding every error every time. Your goal should be to get a little sharper each time you put your editor's eyes and ears to work.

name: ________________ date: ________

Putting on Your Editor's Hat

Whenever you're going to edit, it helps to put on your editor's hat. It's not a real hat. Actually, it's more of an attitude that says, "I'm going to help this writer." Here's a warm-up to get your eyes, ears *and* attitude tuned in. Read the sentences in the example aloud to yourself. Mark any errors you find with the correct editor's mark. Look at the chart from Lesson 22 if you need to.

Its that Time of year when it seems as though. you can you almost here the grass grow. we have a day or two of rain another day of sun and then it's time to mow. Taking care of the grass is job. Part of my allowance comes from mowing the lawn whenever it needs it. At this time of Year, it seems to need it all the time

Number of errors I found ____

Check It Out

Share the results of your edit with a partner. First, compare the *number* of errors you found. Then, see whether each of you found the same errors. Did both of you find the same mistakes? Did you use the same editor's marks? After comparing, make any changes to your editing that you want. If your partner remembered more editor's marks, go ahead and put those in, too.

Number of errors my partner and I found together ____

A Bigger Job

Now that you're warmed up, you are ready for a longer piece of writing. Read this passage aloud to yourself. Use both your eyes and ears to help you edit the writing. Try to use the proper editor's marks. Use the chart on page 98 if you need to.

name: .... date: ....

The workers across street started early. I think it was 7 A.M. when the first truck arrived to drop off Lumber. I know that 7 A.M. is not sooper early, but it a day off from school The noise started with a huge THUD as the lumber slammed onto the pavement the neighbors are adding on to there house, so there were big boreds heavy beams and sheets of plywood. My other neighbors dog started. barking when the truck pulled away. Becase i couldnt sleep anyway, I got dressed and went outside to and watch.

Total number of errors I found ____

Share and Compare

Share your editing results with a partner. How many errors did each of you find? What kinds of errors were they? Did you and your partner use the same editor's marks? If your partner found something you missed or used an editor's mark you had forgotten, mark the necessary changes on your paper. Remember that this practice is a team effort.

Total number of errors my partner and I found together ____

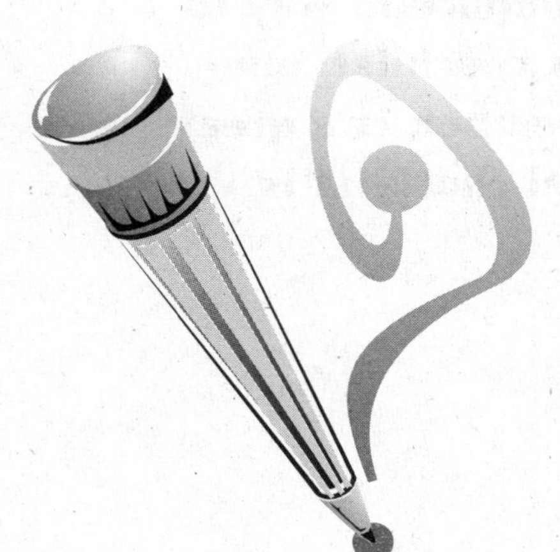

A Writer's Question

What do you think will be the hardest part of editing your own work?

Lesson 24

name: .... date: ....

My Very own Editing Checklist

Editing is one of the important final steps in the writing process. A good editor and a willing writer (sometimes they're the same person) can give a piece of writing the high polish it needs. Knowing which mistakes you make most often is one important way to help cut down on them. A good editor's checklist, one that shows the things you need to remember, is a great tool to have and use. Making a personal checklist is your goal in this lesson.

name: .... date: ....

Beginning with You

To make a useful checklist, you have to be willing to look at your writing honestly. It might help to take one or two pieces of writing from your folder and look them over. List the editing problems that you see or hear most often in your work. Don't skim! Look closely, as if the writing were under a microscope. What's going on in there? Do you notice any missing periods or commas? Do you see any missing capitals? These are editing problems that belong on your list. Don't worry if you can't fill all the lines below. Just be sure to write your main editing problems.

My Editing Checklist

1. ______________________________

2. ______________________________

3. ______________________________

4. ______________________________

5. ______________________________

6. ______________________________

Share and Compare

When you have completed your list, get together with a partner. Share your lists. It's OK if your lists look very different. Did you write down *any* of the same things? Put a **check mark** by any item that appears on both your lists. Did your partner think of anything that you forgot to put on your list?

name: .... date: ....

A Very <u>Classy</u> List

It is likely that several other classmates listed the same editing problems that you and your partner did. Your goal now is to make a list of common editing problems that your class will work on together (a team effort). Your teacher may have an item or two to add to the list, too. The finished list should have several items, but don't make it too long. You'll notice more improvement if you focus your efforts on a few problems instead of trying to fix everything at once.

Putting It to Use

Use the checklist every time you write. Keep a copy of it at your desk or in your notebook where you can find it easily. See how many editing problems from the list you can find each time you edit your work. If you put your eagle eye to work, you won't need to use the list for long!

Warning: As you use your checklist, check off only the items you have actually fixed.

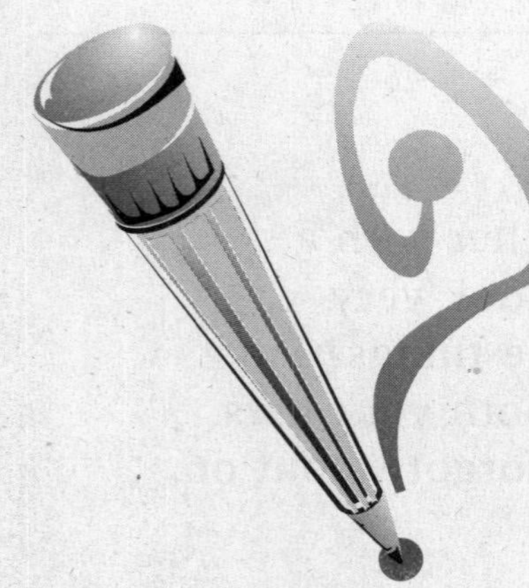

A Writer's Question

Which item from the class checklist also appears on your personal list? Is there something from *your* list that is not on the class list?

Wrap-up Activity 1

Wanted: Some Traits!

Read the "Wanted Poster" description of each trait. Then, from the four choices, pick the trait you think is the best match. Put an **X** by that trait's name.

Wanted: A trait that lives for spotting and correcting errors in spelling, punctuation, grammar, capitalization, and paragraphing. Often travels with a set of editor's marks. This trait's name is

___ Ideas ___ Conventions ___ Voice

___ Sentence Fluency

Wanted: A trait that brags about having a strong main idea and plenty of thumbs-up details. Won't be seen in the company of a villain known as "Filler." This trait's name is

___ Ideas ___ Sentence Fluency ___ Conventions

___ Organization

Wanted: A trait known for strong leads and super conclusions. A real fanatic about having everything in order. This trait's name is

___ Conventions ___ Voice ___ Word Choice

___ Organization

Wanted: A trait that thrives on energy and enthusiasm. Known for its individuality. Often hangs out with strong feelings. This trait's name is

___ Word Choice ___ Voice ___ Organization

___ Sentence Fluency

name: .... date: ....

Wanted: A trait that loves to make your writing fun and easy to read aloud. Spends most of its time creating varied sentence beginnings and making dialogue sound real and natural. Mortal enemy: The dreaded Run-on Sentence! This trait's name is

___ Word Choice ___ Sentence Fluency ___ Ideas

___ Conventions

Wanted: A trait that can usually be found in the company of strong verbs and sensory words (words about sounds, sights, touches, smells, and tastes). Avoids puffed-up, inflated writing at all costs. This trait's name is

___ Conventions ___ Organization

___ Ideas ___ Word Choice

name: .... date: ....

Wrap-up Activity 2

Making a Diagnosis

When the tomato plants wilt or the roses turn brown, the gardener must identify the problem. It could be too much water, not enough water, hungry rabbits, or some other problem. Once the problem is identified, the skilled gardener knows just what to do to fix it.

Writing is very much like this. When you know the six traits, you can use them to diagnose writing problems such as vague details, confusing order, lack of voice, or run-on sentences. You then revise to get rid of those problems.

Read each of the four writing samples. Then decide what you think the main problem is in each piece of writing. Circle *a, b, c,* or *d.* Write your own comments, too. (**Note:** A piece could have more than one problem, but one kind of problem should stand out.)

Sample 1

When we went white-water rafting last summer, it was the coolest thing I have ever done. My mom, my dad, my sister and I all went. It was so cool when we hit the first rapids! I was scared to death, but my dad said to hang on tight. I did hang on tight, and at the end I was glad I went white-water rafting. I knew that I wouldn't be scared to go again. I was really, really happy. I think everyone should have a chance to do something as cool as white-water rafting.

The MAIN problem with Sample 1 is

a. Ideas: The writer's message is not clear.

b. Word Choice: The writer uses some words too many times.

c. Organization: The order of events is very confusing.

d. Conventions: There are many errors in spelling, punctuation, and grammar.

name: .... date: ....

My thoughts about Sample 1: ______________________

____

____

Sample 2

"Hello," said Sean. "My name is Sean. What is your name?"

"I am Gabriella," said Gabriella. "Would you like to play softball now?"

"Oh, yes," said Sean. "I like softball. Where shall we play?"

"Let's play on the field," said Gabriella. "You can meet my other friends."

"Good," said Sean. "Let's go now. I can hardly wait to play."

The MAIN problem with Sample 2 is

a. Ideas: It is hard to tell what these people are talking about.

b. Organization: The two speakers switch topics so much that their conversation is hard to follow.

c. Sentence Fluency: The dialogue does not sound like real people talking.

d. Conventions: The text has many spelling and punctuation errors.

My thoughts about Sample 2: ______________________

____

____

name: .... date: ....

Sample 3

When my dog got hit by a car it was really sad. It was on a Tuesday. He was a really nice dog. His name was Jake. I got him when I was five, I had him a pretty long time. A lot of my friends have pets, too. I hope I will get another dog some day. Jake was a really good dog, I miss him. We used to go on walks a lot. Sometimes my mom would feed him for me if I was too busy.

The MAIN problem with Sample 3 is with

a. Conventions: Too many words are misspelled.

b. Voice: This paper has little emotion or energy.

c. Ideas: There is no main idea so it's hard to know what the writer is trying to tell us.

d. Sentence Fluency: This piece has run-on sentences.

My thoughts about Sample 3: ______________________________

____

____

Sample 4

I will never forget my first day of school, holding onto my mom's hand as though I would never let go. Now, of course, I LOVE school, and you could not keep me home if you tried. When you get older, things do not scare you as much. The scariest thing for me was that I would get lost. The building was so huge, and when you're five, the thought of getting lost terrifies you. Naturally, I do not worry about getting lost anymore. It would be pretty strange if I couldn't find my way around this school by now! It isn't as huge as I used to think. The other thing that frightened me was eating strange food. Would they serve quivering liver or rubbery octopus? I wasn't sure! Thank goodness I bring my own lunch now, and it's usually peanut butter! That's my favorite. Well, bye for now.

name: .... date: ....

The MAIN problem with Sample 4 is with

a. Sentence Fluency: Almost all the sentences begin the same way, and there is one run-on.

b. Word Choice: The writer does not use any interesting words.

c. Organization: The order is confusing and hard to follow.

d. Voice: The writing is pretty flat because the writer sounds so bored with this topic.

My thoughts about Sample 4: ______________________

____

____

Check your answers with your partner. Did you diagnose the problems the same way?